MOVE. NOURISH. BELIEVE.

THE FIT WOMAN'S SECRET REVEALED

© 2011, Lorna Jane Clarkson
Reprint 2012
Published by The Messenger Group Pty Ltd
PO Box H241
Australia Square NSW 1215

A CIP catalogue of this book is available from the National Library of Australia.

Clarkson, Lorna Jane

Move Nourish Believe

ISBN 978-0-9805112-7-7

◻◻◻ LORNA JANE

Lorna Jane
Marketing Manager: Danielle McKenzie
Graphic Designer: Tara McCafferty
Recipe Editor: Hannah Batstone
Food and Profile Photographer: Louise Smit
Fashion Photographers: Jason Zambelli, Henryk Lobaczewski, Michelle Abond, Skeet Booth
www.lornajane.com
www.movenourishbelieve.com

Image of Sheridan Wright courtesy of CLEO. Photography: Marija Ivkovic

Published and Project Managed by The Messenger Group

The Messenger Group
Editor: Sarah Megginson
Copy Editor: Jane O'Sullivan
Creative Director: Claire Cassey
Assistant Designer: Jade Dunwoody
www.themessengergroup.com.au

Printed in China

ACKNOWLEDGEMENTS

I'd like to thank my husband Bill for his constant love, support, vision and devotion to helping me build Lorna Jane. You are my courage, my comfort, my voice of reason and I cannot imagine a day without you in it.

A big thank you to my family and friends for their support and unconditional love, and for being "just a phone call away" for as long as I can remember. Knowing and loving each of you brings me so much joy and happiness, for which I am eternally grateful.

To the Lorna Jane family, from my design and development team, to the warehouse staff, store girls, sales team and everyone else who works each day to help continue to produce and evolve the Lorna Jane brand. Thanks team, you are the best and make it a joy to come to work every day.

And above all, I'd like to thank you, the Lorna Jane customer. The real women out there, who I rely on for inspiration and who I owe the most thanks because you enable me to keep doing what I love every day, and are ultimately responsible for keeping the Lorna Jane dream alive.

CONTENTS

MOVE. NOURISH. BELIEVE.

INTRODUCTION

I have a confession to make: I'm an eternal optimist. It's the way I choose to view the world because experience has proven to me time and time again that if I believe in myself enough, and I'm prepared to work hard, I can reach any goal I set out to achieve.

I'm blessed to wake up every morning feeling energised, happy and raring to go because I truly love the life I have created for myself. That's not to say every day is a breeze – like most women, more often than not, I feel I'm juggling a million different things. I'm an entrepreneur, a fashion designer, a fitness advocate and the Chief Creative Officer of my activewear fashion label, Lorna Jane. I'm also a wife, daughter, sister, aunt and friend, with a close-knit family and busy social life.

So you may ask, what is the secret behind my positive outlook and sunny attitude towards life? Well, that's why I've decided to sit down and write this book. Over the years I've developed a philosophy for enjoying a healthy, active and positive lifestyle and I'm excited to finally share my secrets with you in the hope that it will encourage you to live your best life too.

My mission through Lorna Jane is to inspire active living; this is what drives me day-in, day-out. I live and breathe this concept through my personal philosophy of Move, Nourish, Believe – which is my secret and the three pillars of creating a healthy, joyous and vibrant life.

I **Move** my body every day. I **Nourish** from the inside out. And I truly **Believe** anything is possible.

My goal isn't just to be fit and healthy but to lead a happy life, full of vitality and purpose – and I want you to be inspired to live your best life too. For me Move, Nourish, Believe is the driving force behind what I do, and it's a mantra you can adopt in your own life. In this book you'll discover the 'Fit Woman's Secret' and uncover the key to living each day to the fullest.

It starts with Move, moving every day is vital to keep your body in fighting fit shape. I'll reveal some tips and secrets to motivate you into action.

Next comes Nourish, the food you eat has a huge impact on how you think, feel, move and sleep. When you read what I have to say about nourishing your body and spirit, I guarantee you'll be as passionate as I am about eating nutritious food that propels you forward in all areas of life.

And finally, Believe, I genuinely believe that we can all have what we desire in life; in fact, I'm living proof of that. I want to show you how to have the kind of faith in yourself that compels you to reach for the stars, knowing that you can achieve your dreams and live the life you imagined – that is, if you're willing to put in the hard work.

My hope is that after reading this book, you'll come away feeling inspired to be active, motivated, hopeful and brimming with energy to live your best life. I want this book to inspire you and I want you to enjoy reading it but at the same time, I want you to realise just how serious I am about helping you transform your life. Throughout these pages, I'll share tips, secrets and learnings I've picked up over the years, and they'll hopefully reinforce some things you already know... and ideally, show

IF YOU CAN DREAM IT YOU CAN DO IT.

- WALT DISNEY

you that if you make just a few adjustments, you can fundamentally shift the way you live and leave unhelpful habits behind.

If you're already on this journey, you'll understand when I say that prioritising your own health and fitness leads only to good things. It kicks off a chain reaction of events in your mind, body and spirit, and the positive changes that flow through to the rest of your life can be enormous.

If you're new to the idea of embracing active living, then take a deep breath, make a strong resolution to yourself, and trust me when I say jump in 100%. If this is what you want for yourself, don't waste time comparing your life to mine (or anyone else's for that matter) and start making positive changes today. Do it dramatically and with as much fanfare as possible, and know that if you bring intensity and passion to your new commitments, you will reach your goals. When failure is not an option, you can (and will) achieve great things.

The truth is, the process of change isn't hard; it just takes dedication and constant commitment to put yourself and your own wellbeing first, but once you get started, you'll actually find it's addictive. The exercise part might be difficult to achieve every day, and you may miss your daily chocolate fix, but as your attitude shifts and you begin making positive changes for your health, you'll see the results flow through to every part of your

life. I promise you will be asking yourself, "Why didn't I do this earlier?"

I'm not saying it's always easy. Change takes courage, it can be tough at times, but the *Move, Nourish, Believe* philosophy is fun to follow and, best of all, it works. Remember that every single day, life presents us with choices; some seem forgettable and insignificant while others are life changing, but it's what you do with each of these choices that really matters. I've made many decisions over the years, some good, some not so good, but each one was made with conviction at the time and a belief that it was right. When an opportunity presents itself my initial response is often, "What have I got to lose?" However, not everything works out as you planned but with an optimistic mindset you can normally find positives in most situations. And when you think about it, some of the best stories we tell people are about the more challenging times in our lives. Have the courage to take chances and allow yourself to slip up from time to time. We can't always know the outcome of our decisions but we must learn from these experiences and, if nothing else, they make great anecdotes for your family, friends and colleagues.

We experienced plenty of "learning curves" in the early days of building the Lorna Jane brand which we can laugh about now. Starting a business is never a walk in the park and it takes hard work and sacrifice. I'm lucky

I was able to take my passion and turn it into a successful enterprise but I also believe that if you love what you do, and you're willing to put sweat and tears into making it a reality, then the rest will fall into place.

Money has never been a motivation for me in making Lorna Jane successful. Those close to me know that I believe if you concentrate on doing what you love, then success will come. For me, being fit and healthy everyday, and inspiring other people to do the same, is what propels me forward.

That's why, to this day, the most exciting part of what I do is seeing my thoughts, concepts and designs in the real world, becoming a part of people's lives. I get a thrill from seeing anyone wearing Lorna Jane because it means that in some way I have influenced them towards leading an active life, which is what we're all about. I understand my customers have so many choices as to how and where to spend their money, so I consider it a compliment that they have chosen to wear my designs.

When I see someone wearing Lorna Jane, I want to talk to them, ask questions and thank them for supporting our brand. I love receiving feedback and hearing that what I do can change people's lives for the better. In a world where the need for a healthy lifestyle is more prominent than ever, I am driven by how I can help and inspire women to get moving.

I never tire of seeing people wearing Lorna Jane. In the early days, women in my classes wore Lorna Jane and it always gave me a buzz but there's one memory that stands out. I was sitting in Starbucks in Hong Kong and two locals walked past head-to-toe in Lorna Jane. I felt surprise, followed by delight, and then a lingering feeling of overwhelming happiness. I was alone and if anyone had been watching my facial expressions, they would have thought I was crazy. It was unexpected because I was far from home and it reinforced my belief that what we were creating was something that could be loved by women the world over.

It may sound strange, but I think of the women who wear Lorna Jane as being part of a "sisterhood". A network of women who embrace a healthy lifestyle, who care about fashion as much as they do about fitness and want to help influence other women to think the same way. Today, my desire is to expand this "sisterhood" and spread our message far and wide. I hope Lorna Jane can become synonymous with active living on a global scale so that all women can achieve their best lives.

I'm constantly searching for ways I can do better and feel it's my responsibility to ensure Lorna Jane lives up to your expectations. Every garment I create is woven with the *Move, Nourish, Believe* philosophy in mind, to inspire us all to live our best, most beautiful life. At the end of the day, I too am a Lorna Jane customer; I design clothing that motivates me to be active, healthy and balanced – hopefully in doing this, I can inspire you to do the same.

Yours in active living,

Lorna Jane xx

BUSINESS ENTREPRENEUR, FITNESS ADVOCATE AND FASHION DESIGNER

"My life in five words is... non-stop, creative, active, inspiring and happy."

WHERE IT ALL BEGAN

Growing up I was a happy child. If you ask my mum, she'll tell you that I was always smiling and content to go with the flow. However, I was quite fussy about what I wore. I remember being five years old and mum took me shopping, I picked out the dresses I liked and the dresses I didn't. I guess even at an early age I knew what I liked when it came to fashion.

I always had a clear idea of what I wanted to wear and if I couldn't find what I liked, I just made it myself. My girlfriends loved it because as a teenager I would sit on the beach and crochet bikinis for them. I loved being creative and playing around with the latest looks.

Although I loved clothes, I wasn't always active – at least, not until I moved to Australia. I was born in northern England, in a small village called Orrell. My dad actually still lives there in the same house I was born in. It was a lovely upbringing but the truth is, I was more of an indoors, book-reading type. I have fond memories of walking to Sunday school with my sister Julie and feeding the ducks at the pond in my wellies, and other memories of getting a new bike for Christmas and having to be content with riding it up and down the hallway because it was snowing outside. I think I did more lifting of my bike to turn it around than actual riding.

It all changed when I moved to Australia at the age of 10. I was inspired by the outdoors lifestyle to be more active because at almost any time of the year I could ride my bike, or play in the yard, or run in the park. My passion for being fit and active kicked in, so I signed up for cheerleading in high school. I loved the dance aspect of cheering but the bonus was, I got to attend all the school sporting events, without having to compete.

Ask my friends and family and they will tell you that I don't enjoy competitive sports. It's strange, considering how driven I am with my business, but I'm not all that interested in "winning". My philosophy is (and has always been) that you should try to be the very best version of "you" that you can be and you don't need to compete with others to achieve that.

I never considered myself the most talented girl, or the sportiest, or the fittest or the most beautiful. Actually, I've always been pretty average. But I was determined and I always believed in myself. I think this has a lot to do with the wonderful friends and positive people in my life. I cherish my friendships and cannot imagine life without some of my dearest girlfriends. We are in each other's corner no matter what, celebrating victories and offering support, because our friendships are based on love, respect and a genuine desire to help each other reach for the stars. My experience has always been that true friendships stand the test of time and don't need daily communication or hard work to keep them alive. Real friends are the ones who are always in your corner with words of encouragement or an honest opinion when needed.

My mum has always been my biggest cheerleader and after high school it was mum who suggested I become a dental therapist. Like most teenagers, I wasn't sure what I wanted to do with my life. I had a love of fashion that needed financing and this seemed as good a career choice as any. At the time I was getting caught up in the whole aerobics craze so I completed my Aerobic Instructor Training certificate at the same time. I began teaching classes at nights and on weekends, little did I know that this was just the beginning of a life long love affair with fitness, health and active living.

A few years later, at the age of 20, I moved from Brisbane to Cairns. It was life changing for me. I'd finished my dental training with the Queensland government and Cairns was my first posting. Moving to Cairns and out of my family home was a big deal for me and most definitely forced me to be independent. I had to find my own place, make new friends and start a new life for myself. If ever I had to draw on my own sense of self-belief, this was it.

It was tough in the beginning but slowly, my new-found independence started to feel good. My days were packed. I was working full-time, teaching aerobics at night and on weekends, and also baking healthy treats for a local café. Looking back now, I can see the beginnings of the *Move, Nourish, Believe* concept starting to develop in how I was living my life.

Back then there were only a few brands to choose from when it came to activewear and, as I'm sure some of you will remember, it was mainly black leotards and shiny leggings, in stock standard shapes and designs. If you wanted something different you had to get it made to measure at your local ballet shop and even then, it was just one of the ballet mums stitching it together on her sewing machine at home.

I knew what I liked to wear: bright, colourful clothes that not only fitted well but that made me feel good. I grew frustrated that I couldn't find any activewear that fit this description and I was sick of wearing the same old thing to every class. So, I created my first leotard pattern (yes, it's embarrassing to admit it but that's what I really wanted to wear back then) by getting my favourite swimsuit, pulling it apart and laying it on some newspaper.

I'd never formally learnt to sew but I taught myself through trial and error. As always my determination got me through. My flatmate was a high school home economics teacher, so she helped teach me what I needed to know. Working with stretch fabrics could be so frustrating – sometimes I'd get so fed up that I would throw the leotard I was stitching together out the window. But I picked up the basics quickly enough and I got better with time.

Always smiling, even from an early age.

Growing up in England, me with my grandad, sister and younger cousins.

Practising to become a dental therapist.

"I Move, Nourish and Believe every day."

Opening stores in the early days.

Us on our Wedding Day.

Publicity shot with some of our Fashion Awards.

When I wore my designs people immediately began asking, "Where did you get that?" When I confessed I'd made them myself, friends and then the women in my aerobics classes asked me to create leotards and leggings for them too.

I started making custom-designed activewear in between everything else. To say I was "busy" is an understatement. I'd wake at 5am and cut out newspaper patterns before work and then I was on the sewing machine that night after leading an aerobics class, working until one or two in the morning.

I spent six months like this making up to 20 leotards a week. No one wanted to be seen in the same thing, so I was challenged creatively to constantly come up with new concepts and patterns.

The hours were long, but I was having fun. I relished the opportunity to create my own activewear and still couldn't believe that other people wanted to wear them. These were women who came to my classes every week and trusted me to guide them with their fitness, so I felt some pressure to deliver garments they really loved. I think that's why I'm so customer focused today, because I still feel that sense of wanting to really please my customers.

Around this time I met my husband, Bill, through some friends. Cairns is a small place and we kept bumping into one another. He was good looking, funny, interesting to talk to and kind. Best of all, he loved sport, was fit, and lived an active lifestyle. We hit it off from the beginning and it was love at first sight – for me, anyway.

It was almost a case of bad timing because after five years in Cairns, I had decided to move back to Brisbane. I was 25 years old and ready for a new challenge and, as much as I loved my independence, I also missed my family. By the time Bill asked me out, I had already arranged my transfer back to Brisbane so our date was more a farewell dinner than anything else. One of my fondest memories of that time was of Bill sprinting to the airport as my plane was being called to wish me a last minute goodbye. He made me promise to call him when I landed, and when I got onto that plane I could hardly wipe the smile off my face.

After that, weekly phone calls turned to daily catch-ups, and within a year Bill had sold his house, sold his business and was living in Brisbane. I later found out it was love at first sight for Bill, too, and what an amazing journey it has been. A true love affair based on mutual admiration and respect, we encourage each other to pursue our dreams and we believe anything is possible, as long as we have each other. It's been a love that has kept us together through everything that life has thrown at us, and a love that I'm grateful for every single day.

QUITTING THE 9 TO 5

There was never a real plan to launch Lorna Jane as a fashion business. I just had a dream about waking up every day being passionate about what I did with my time and, ultimately, how I would live my life.

In those early days, it wasn't about being successful or building an inspirational brand, it was just about being able to do what made me happy. Now 21 years later I can reflect on the choices I made and I'm so glad I had the determination and self-belief to make it happen – but it wasn't always easy.

My first difficult decision came when I moved back to Brisbane and Lorna Jane orders started flooding in. I was realising that there were a whole lot of women out there who felt the same way as I did about activewear and how they wanted to live their lives. I had to decide whether I believed in my concept enough to quit my job and turn it into a real business. I was nervous about giving up the security of a full-time job and some of my friends and family thought I was crazy to even contemplate quitting to follow my dream.

You have to remember, this was back in the late 80s and early 90s when the economy was in the doldrums and mortgage interest rates were near 20%. Everyone was focused on "stability" and "security" and I was venturing into the unknown, into an industry that didn't really exist. I had to trust my gut instinct and believe in what I was doing.

One of the owners of a gym I was teaching at suggested I take some space in his centre, which meant I could have a small studio and showroom for Lorna Jane activewear. The rent was manageable and he kindly offered me reception work at the gym, so I had some income to rely on until business took off. I decided to take a leap of faith and quit my job. Within a week, my shop was up and running. I guess you could say this was my first retail store – even though it was on the third floor of a fitness centre, overlooking an alleyway, and opening on to one of Brisbane's most popular aerobics studios at the time.

As it turned out, I only needed to work on reception for a total of three weeks, as orders quickly piled up faster than I could make the garments. It was then I realised: hold on, Lorna, you might really be on to something.

FAILURE IS NOT AN OPTION

Before long my days were "crazy-busy," so I hired a couple of people to delegate cutting and sewing to, including an amazing woman, Karen Hellmech. She had been sewing swimwear for some of the big players of the time and her wealth of knowledge – and more importantly, her willingness to share it with me – really did lay the foundation for the quality standards we have in our business today. Twenty one years later Karen is still an important part of the Lorna Jane family and works in our production team at head office.

I must confess that although the design side of the business came naturally to me, the business side was another story. Tax time rolled around and I handed over a manila folder stuffed with dockets and receipts to my tax guy. "Lorna, you really need to take this more seriously," he said. "If you don't start managing your business better, you could get into trouble."

For me, failure was never an option; I knew that no matter what happened, I would get back up and keep moving forward. This is where the infamous Lorna Jane motto, NEVER, NEVER, NEVER GIVE UP was forged. But at this point, I'll admit that I felt utterly overwhelmed. Although I loved making activewear and coming up with new designs, the business side was wearing me down. I got home and said to Bill, "This isn't fun anymore."

Fortunately, Bill is a big picture sort of guy and he loves a challenge. He had previously owned businesses so when I was feeling weighed down by the business side of things, he stepped in and said, "Why don't you keep doing the design work that you love and I'll look after the paperwork?"

When I look back, I can see it was a courageous move on Bill's part. Not many men could come into their wife's business and sell leotards. Not to mention the fact we would now have to rely on Lorna Jane completely to give us our income. Luckily our skill sets were complementary, the balance was perfect and to this day, it's been his entrepreneurial spirit and constant support that has helped shape the business. It's been wonderful working on this dream together and I am grateful every day that I get to go on this amazing journey, weather the challenges and celebrate the achievements with the man of my dreams.

SELLING THE DREAM HOME, TO LIVE THE DREAM

Sometimes when you're following your dreams, and in our case building a business, you do things that may not seem entirely logical to your family and friends at the time. We've definitely made choices and done things over the years which our friends and family thought were insane. Around the year 2000, we made another one of these decisions.

We had moved production from our home to a small factory in Kelvin Grove, but we were already "bursting at the seams". We needed to move to a bigger factory but there was only one way we could afford it: by selling our dream home.

Our plan had been to create a home where we could spend the rest of our lives together. We had meticulously renovated it every weekend for seven years and you could even see the church where we were married from the back deck. We knew if we were to take the business to the next level we had to sell the house. Looking back, the decision wasn't that hard. We were never home anyway and ate most of our meals at the factory, and we knew without a doubt that we could always buy a

"We lived on-site for six years and when we moved out, we converted our apartment into office space. Our old master bedroom is now my office."

WE ALL HAVE OUR OWN **LIFE** TO PURSUE, OUR OWN KIND OF **DREAM** TO BE WEAVING AND WE ALL HAVE SOME POWER TO MAKE **WISHES** COME TRUE, AS LONG AS WE KEEP **BELIEVING.**

- LOUISA MAY ALCOTT

house later when the business found its feet. Our idea was to live on-site in a studio apartment attached to the factory. After 18 months of searching, we found a building in Fortitude Valley, back when "the Valley" wasn't considered a "safe" part of town. The factory had been abandoned for years so it was neglected, rotting and full of termites, but it was cheap. So we sold our house and used the proceeds to buy the factory outright and renovate it to basic living and working standards.

While we were moving into our factory, most of our friends were in their second, more substantial homes, creating comfortable lives for themselves. They thought we were crazy but to give credit where credit's due, they could see how much we believed in what we were doing, so they didn't utter one word of discouragement or criticism; you've got to love supportive friends.

Fortunately, our leap of faith paid off. Within a couple of years the building increased in value and the bank allowed us to borrow against it for a business loan. Over the years, as Fortitude Valley transformed into a sought-after suburb, our factory became more and more valuable – and the banks continued to lend us money, secured against the building. Ultimately, buying that factory is the smartest thing we ever did because without it, Lorna Jane wouldn't exist as it does today.

CREATING AN AUTHENTIC BRAND

When I first began designing Lorna Jane, it was all about feeding my passion for fashion-forward activewear. I was creating garments I wanted to wear and that made me look good and feel great. Ultimately, I think this is what gives the Lorna Jane brand its heart and authenticity today because it started life, and is still to this day, product that I genuinely want to wear. The definition of authenticity is being true to yourself and, as a namesake brand, Lorna Jane is 100% true to who I am and what I value as a person.

Fashion is often dismissed as being frivolous or flighty, but on closer inspection it's clear that fashion is an important part of our lives. As modern women, what we wear and the way we choose to present ourselves reveals so much about our attitudes, beliefs and personalities. Fashion can motivate us to lead a better life, which can be both powerful and empowering. When you choose to wear Lorna Jane, you are telling the world you value health and fitness, that you are positive and energetic and determined to live your best life through active living, that you put yourself and the ones you love first and that you know you deserve the best out of life – no compromises.

It's pretty clear that I always believed in our product; I even put my name to the brand to show that I was creating things that I was proud of and that I believed in. When we first launched, activewear as a fashion category didn't even exist. When we thought about marketing our garments, it was difficult to figure out where we "fit".

We couldn't find boutiques that were as passionate about active living as we were and department stores didn't offer the service or product knowledge that I wanted for my customers. On top of this our challenge was, if we did make our way into a department store, where would they put us? We didn't want to be seen as another sports brand because Lorna Jane is about so much more than simply exercise.

We needed a space that reflected a "women only" environment and conveyed the message that it's possible to show you care just as much about fashion as you do about sport. We had no option but to take Lorna Jane direct to the people through our own stores. You have to remember that this was a new concept at the time. Traditionally activewear was sold in masculine environments or squashed amongst the swimwear in department stores. My vision was something completely different to the traditional retail environment. I wanted Lorna Jane to provide an experience where customers could learn about the features and benefits of each garment and leave with activewear to enhance their active life, rather than just picking up a pair of leggings.

Our next challenge was reaching a wider market. We were making five garments of each design to maintain originality but were looking for ways to make 100, or even 200, and still retain that sense of uniqueness and individuality for our customers.

We realised we had to go back to basics and reach out to people in Sydney, Melbourne and Adelaide who were just like me: aerobics instructors who were passionate about fitness. We slowly expanded into other states by "seeding" the product through experienced fitness instructors who were vouching for our brand and selling it to their clients. They fully embraced the concept because it allowed them to give up their day jobs, while helping us to expand in an authentic way. We were able to produce up to 200 of one garment by spreading it thinly across the country and thereby keep its uniqueness.

Through all of this I learnt a great deal about women and today I can confidently say I understand what women want when it comes to fashion. The modern woman is discerning and needs constant inspiration, which is why we create monthly collections of up to 100 pieces. Trust me, the creative, production and logistics process of this is a nightmare, but that is not the point. Bill and I realised long ago there is only one person that counts when it comes to Lorna Jane, and that is the Lorna Jane customer. She is the one who inspires me to turn on creatively day after day and create collections that are even better than the last.

If the Lorna Jane customer wants monthly collections, that is what she will get. If getting her to buy a new inspirational singlet every month with a new motivational message is all I need to do to help her get out of bed with a spring in her step to hit the treadmill, then I will do this until the day I die.

Many people and many businesses have tried to emulate us over the years but more often than not, they struggle to find their feet, and I believe it's because you can't fake authenticity. I am true to my values and every decision I make for the Lorna Jane brand is driven by my own beliefs and my desire to motivate others to live their best life. I would offer the same advice here as I would to any woman in my life: we are all born originals, so why is it that most of us die copies? If you have a business and want to make it resonate with your customers, be true to your own personal values. You will find that your moral compass is often the best guide in making business decisions that strengthen your brand.

It was by following my instincts and staying true to my personal philosophies that the Lorna Jane brand grew. We opened new

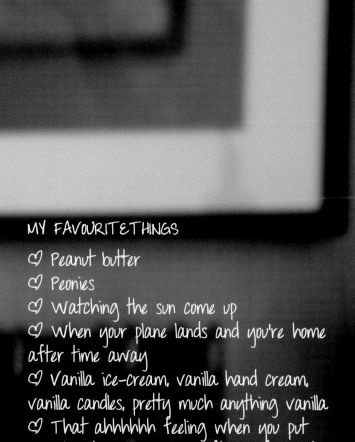

MY FAVOURITE THINGS

♡ Peanut butter
♡ Peonies
♡ Watching the sun come up
♡ When your plane lands and you're home after time away
♡ Vanilla ice-cream, vanilla hand cream, vanilla candles, pretty much anything vanilla
♡ That ahhhhhh feeling when you put your head on your pillow after a full and rewarding day

xx

stores to keep up with demand and by 2003, we were opening two stores every year. Then, suddenly, our growth exploded. We opened store after store after store, and we now launch one new shop every two weeks.

It's a very exciting time for Lorna Jane and our next step is to expand internationally. We've already opened in South Africa and our sights are now set on the United States. However the journey is far from over here in Australia. We continue to face many challenges but are committed to encourage all women to move, nourish and believe every day.

There's also a new generation of girls waiting in the wings, needing guidance on how to be their best and true self. I want Lorna Jane to be there for them – to empower them, as we've done with so many others – and to help and encourage them to live their best life.

2000
◦ Lorna Jane celebrates 10 years in business and moves to new HQ in Fortitude Valley, Brisbane

◦ RAQ Award for Lifestyle Collections

◦ A young Miranda Kerr models in the Lorna Jane look book

1992
◦ Lorna stops teaching aerobics classes as the business takes up more of her time

1996
◦ Lorna Jane opens third store in Cairns, Far North Queensland

1994
◦ Lorna Jane wins the first of many RAQ Fashion Awards for Active Sportswear

1989
◦ Lorna starts making activewear for herself and people in her classes

1998
◦ RAQ Award for Lifestyle Collections

1990
◦ Lorna quits her day job and opens for business on the top floor of a fitness centre

1995
◦ Awarded Myer Award of Excellence, RAQ Award for Active Sportswear and RAQ Award for Swimwear

◦ Lorna Jane opens second store on Queensland's Gold Coast

1997
◦ RAQ Award for Lifestyle Collections

◦ First interstate store opens on Sydney's fashion strip Oxford Street

1999
◦ RAQ Award for Excellence in Manufacture, and RAQ Award for Swimwear

1993
◦ First retail store in Brisbane's Broadway Mall opens

2004

◦ Receives The Queensland 400 certificate recognising outstanding achievement in business and its contribution to QLD's economic growth

◦ 20th store opens in Melbourne

◦ Lorna Jane's iconic Flashdance Pants were first released

TWENTY ONE YEARS ON

2009

◦ Eight new stores in NSW, VIC and WA bringing the total number nationwide to 65

2007

◦ Lorna Jane launches its first ever national brand campaign

2011

◦ 100th store opens in Little Collins Street in Melbourne, VIC

◦ Lorna Jane wins AMP Capital & BRW magazine's Outstanding Retailer of the Year Award

◦ Lorna Jane launches its Academy of Retail Excellence

◦ Lorna Jane South Africa opens for business

2006

◦ The Never Never Never Give Up singlet is released for the first time

2008

◦ 50th store opens in Paddington, QLD

◦ Launched Little Miss Lorna Jane range to inspire future generations to be active

2010

◦ CHAMP VENTURES buys minority stake in Lorna Jane

◦ 70th store opens

◦ Lorna Jane launches first LJ Black luxury capsule collection

◦ Lorna Jane wins Website Award

MOVE. NOURISH. BELIEVE.

WE DO NOT STOP EXERCISING WHEN WE GET OLD, WE GET OLD BECAUSE WE STOP EXERCISING.

- DR KENNETH COOPER

I like leading an active life and I'm committed to moving my body every day because I love how it makes me feel. Can you believe it was only around 20 years ago that humans would take, on a daily basis, an average of 10,000 steps? Today, most of us barely take more than a few hundred. As we've moved into the 21st century with all of its conveniences, like escalators, public transport and remote controls, many of us seem to have reduced the amount of moving we do every day.

Think about it, how much have you moved in the last 24 hours? You might catch the train or drive to work, then sit at a desk all day and commute home, before spending the night on the sofa. If any of this sounds familiar, your answer is probably "very little".

Now let's talk about moving your body every day. If you take anything away from this book, I hope it's this: the most important thing you can do for yourself is to move every day. I want you to be the very best version of yourself, so at least give it a go... for your heart, for your mind and for your body.

It doesn't have to be anything drastic to begin with. Kick things off by going for a brisk 30-minute walk, or run around with your kids in the backyard for 20 minutes, or jump on the treadmill before breakfast. It's okay to start small. But you need to do something – anything – each and every day that moves your body, gets your heart racing and tells every single cell in your body that you're alive.

FINDING THE MOTIVATION TO MOVE

I know from personal experience that finding motivation to get moving can be difficult. The truth is, there's no fail-safe motivational secret, as everyone is different. However I'd love to share my personal philosophies in the hope they offer you a healthy boost of inspiration and encouragement to get active.

SET A TIME THAT WORKS FOR YOU

We are creatures of habit. We crave routine, so a great idea is to figure out the best time of day that suits you to get active and make it a standing appointment. It may be tough at first but a routine becomes habit very quickly, your body will switch onto autopilot in no time at all.

Personally for me, mornings are my time to shine. I exercise first thing every morning because I know that if I don't, I may not get around to it later in the day. Mornings may not work for you but no matter how busy your daily routine, there will be a way to incorporate movement if you are really committed.

ADOPT THE RIGHT MINDSET

You might feel you have so much going on that even carving out 20 minutes for a quick stretch or work-out before work seems impossible. When you're in that mindset, exercise seems like just another thing to add to your "to do" list and clutter up your schedule.

CHANGE HAPPENS WHEN WE VENTURE OVER THE EDGE AND TAKE ONE SMALL STEP AT A TIME.

Instead, don't focus on what exercise "takes" from you – time – but look at what it gives you. I don't view exercise simply as a way to burn off calories but rather as a way to get my circulation going, to build new tissue and to function at a higher metabolic rate during the day. That way, being active is a non-negotiable part of my day, just like having a shower, brushing my teeth and going to work.

I once heard someone refer to being active as "giving them time" because the vitality they gain from exercising actually gives them hours of productive energy. For me, this is absolutely true. Hop on the treadmill for 30 minutes when you're tired and you'll gain four hours of renewed energy.

CREATE POSITIVE RITUALS

I have many daily and weekly rituals that keep me moving, but it is my weekend ritual that I truly cherish. Every Saturday and Sunday, Bill and I take our dog Roger for a long walk along the beach to our favourite café. It is an energising start to the morning and gives us time to plan the day or week ahead and earn our breakfast calories at the same time. I usually order a good cup of black coffee with two poached eggs or a veggie omelette. One of the things I enjoy is that we get to exercise and enjoy breakfast without any time constraints, which to me is what weekends are all about. It's not difficult to create an enjoyable ritual like this in your own life. You just need to figure out what works for you and your family, what gets you moving and, most importantly, you need to make it fun.

WEAR THE RIGHT CLOTHES

My philosophy is to always be ready to move in whatever I'm wearing. If I plan on doing exercise after work, I wear a crop top and singlet to the office with a tailored jacket. At 5pm, all I need to do is change my pants and pop on a pair of sneakers and I'm ready to go. I do the same on weekends if I want to go shopping or meet friends for lunch followed by a gym work-out. This concept is what Lorna Jane is all about; I design activewear with this type of lifestyle in mind.

By wearing clothes that allow me to move at a moment's notice, I'm always ready to take the active approach. I find I'm actually more creative when I'm wearing comfortable clothes. I feel less constricted and more relaxed so I can sit on the floor, spread paperwork out around me, jump up and move around the room if I need to.

UNLOCK YOUR PASSION

Trust me, you won't stick at something if you feel like it's hard work or you don't enjoy it. If you want great legs but you hate running, don't give up – just find an alternative. If you love the hype of a spin class or the energy and escapism of the neighbourhood dance class, you will be more likely to commit. As a result you will enjoy your exercise, have fun and improve your physique along the way.

GET MOVING

You want to get moving but you don't know where to start. Here are just a few suggestions;

▱ Do aerobic exercise that makes you sweat and raises your heart rate. Running, cycling, power walking, hot yoga... all of these fit the bill.

▱ Get involved in strength training, which uses weights to improve your muscle, bone and ligament strength. All through my 20s I thought that cardio was the way forward, but I was wrong. It's strength training that is absolutely essential. If you can get good muscle tone when you're young, you'll hold on to that shape for longer as you age. If only I knew back then what I know now.

▱ Take your dog, partner, friend or kids for a brisk walk. Walking is a great way to clear the mental cobwebs, or catch up on the latest news and gossip. There's a reason I put out an inspirational singlet with the slogan, "I love my 3km talk" because I actually do. Most of the time, I'm so busy talking I hardly realise I'm exercising.

▱ Try a class at the local gym. I find that classes and group exercise in general are a great motivator. You're more likely to work hard in a class environment and there is less chance of you throwing in the towel halfway through with the rest of the class there to see you quit.

MY DAILY ROUTINE

move

My routine actually starts the night before. I always set myself up for the next day by laying out my activewear to change into when I wake up. It's the first thing I see when I get out of bed, so it's an instant visual reminder that it's time to get into gear. If I wake up and *don't* exercise, I feel really ordinary when I see the clothes sitting there later that day. As a motivational tool, it works a treat.

I'm usually in bed with a good book by 10pm, so I can get a solid night's sleep and still wake up rested and refreshed the next morning at 5am. I like to start my day slowly by giving myself at least an hour to do whatever I like - check my iPad, play with my dog Roger, run through my diary and eat breakfast while watching the news.

By 6am, I'm ready to exercise. Whether it's putting on a work-out DVD at home, meeting my trainer for some strength training, or catching up with a friend for a brisk walk, I spend the next 60 to 90 minutes doing something active.

I know many of you are reading this thinking, "But you woke up at 5am! I love my sleep-ins and I could never give them up." I guess this is where you have to figure out what works for you, and prioritise what's most important.

For me, having that time to myself in the morning allows me to recharge and prepare myself to take on whatever comes my way for the rest of the day, so it's well worth the early call time.

nourish

believe

Early mornings may not be your ideal window. If your kids are up at the crack of dawn, it might work better to claim midday for yourself, when they're at school or napping. Or give yourself some time each night to wind down slowly, by riding your exercise bike while you watch your favourite TV program. My guilty pleasure is reality TV shows, I record them to watch whilst I'm on the treadmill. It makes the time go by quickly and I often find myself doing a longer work-out than originally planned so I can see the end of a particular show.

One of the biggest complaints we have as modern women is that we don't have enough time because we're busy juggling work, families, friends, pets, hobbies and households. Trying to squeeze exercise into that mix may seem tricky at first. If this sounds like you, then why not schedule some time into your calendar to get moving? It's time to get honest. Are you really saying you can't fit 30 minutes of exercise into your day? Remember, no excuses. If you don't make a commitment, you'll inevitably find something else to do with your time, so treat this appointment seriously and show up for yourself.

Whatever time of day you settle on, make sure you use it to do something fun and active. Take baby steps by aiming for 30 minutes per day to begin with. Once the routine is established, build from there.

PROMISE YOURSELF TO BE SO
YOUR PEACE OF MIND. LOC
AND MAKE YOUR OPTIMISM
WORK ONLY FOR THE BEST,
THE MISTAKES OF THE
ACHIEVEMENTS OF THE
IMPROVEMENT OF YOURSELF
OTHERS. LIVE IN THE FAITH THAT
SO LONG AS YOU A

RONG THAT NOTHING CAN DISTURB
T THE **SUNNY SIDE** OF EVERYTHING
ME TRUE. THINK ONLY OF THE **BEST**,
D EXPECT ONLY THE **BEST**. FORGET
T AND PRESS ON TO THE GREATER
UTURE. GIVE SO MUCH TIME TO THE
AT YOU HAVE NO TIME TO CRITICISE
E WHOLE WORLD IS ON YOUR SIDE
TRUE TO THE BEST THAT IS IN YOU.

– CHRISTIAN D LARSON

SAY IT OUT LOUD

One of my close friends once confided that when she sets herself a new goal, she doesn't tell anyone about it. "If I tell everyone I'm starting something new and then I don't stick to it, I'm going to feel embarrassed," she told me.

The way I see it, that's the perfect reason why you should tell everyone about your goals. If you're already thinking about failing before you even set sail, how committed are you to really sticking with your plans?

When I'm trying to reach a new goal, my philosophy is to say it out loud and tell as many people as I possibly can, because then I can be held accountable.

Everyone in my life knows this about me - and I mean, everyone. I recently told the barista at my local café that I was on a super cleanse diet. I spill the beans to everyone because I want to succeed. There's no bigger motivation than being accountable for your actions.

HOW TO BANISH THE EXCUSES

Excuse: I have the best intentions to exercise but I always run out of time.
Solution: This is probably the most common excuse we use but the truth is, we can make time if we really want to. If you know you're prone to making excuses, find a reliable friend to exercise with so you're accountable to each other. Every Friday morning I walk with a girlfriend, it's our special time together that we use to catch up on what has been happening in our lives and we never miss it. Knowing that she is waiting for me with all of her news makes me look forward to it. The fact that we are exercising is the added bonus.

Excuse: It's too cold/wet/dark to exercise outdoors.
Solution: If it looks like it's going to rain tomorrow and you'd planned on a morning walk, have a back up. It really comes down to planning. You can put an umbrella next to your work-out gear when you go to bed, or make the decision to do a yoga work-out at home instead. Don't let yourself get away with doing nothing just because you weren't organised. Remember too that doing exercise is a quick and easy way to warm yourself up when you're cold because it gets your blood pumping and warms you from the inside out.

Excuse: My clothes fit me fine and I'm okay with how I look right now, so I can ease back on exercise for the moment.
Solution: Don't hide the results of a not-so-healthy lifestyle under layers of clothing. Put your health first and celebrate with a body you can be proud of. It can be easy to link size and weight with our health, but being active is just as important for your heart and mind as it is for your appearance. There was a time when I wasn't as fit and healthy as I wanted to be and I became an expert at finding the right clothes to "hide" my flaws. That way, I didn't have to exercise as much because I looked fine in my clothes anyway. I've come to realise that these type of outfits do me no favours – because they let me get away with looking and feeling just "okay" instead of living my best life – so I got rid of them. Entering into my 40s, I was sliding into that mindset that as I aged I should expect and accept that my body will change. In my line of work I constantly hear from women who are older and wiser than me but who have been dedicated to maintaining their fitness. They gave me all the proof I needed that age was no barrier (remember, no excuses) and now, my body is better than it was 10 years ago.

Excuse: I've been naughty this weekend, so I'll start my new health and fitness regime on Monday.
Solution: Ah, the perennial Monday that never comes. The way I see it, every single day we have the opportunity to start fresh and to make good choices, regardless of what we did yesterday, or the day before, or last week, or at breakfast this morning. So rather than "starting on Monday" with your new commitment to moving and being active, why not start today? This afternoon? Right now?

Excuse: I don't have time in the mornings and I'm too tired at night to exercise.
Solution: This is an easy go-to excuse and most of the time, you feel validated using it – when you're busy at work and looking after your family and doing everything else, it feels like "something's gotta give" and today that something is exercise. To try and counteract this, firstly, think about your priorities. How important is it to you to look and feel your best? I would say that for most women, it is pretty high on the agenda. Next, I suggest that you set yourself up for success as much as possible. If your treadmill is packed away under the bed, you're less likely to spontaneously jump on it when you have a spare moment, so set it up in your bedroom or lounge. Stack your yoga and fitness DVDs somewhere visible and easy to reach, rather than jammed at the back of your entertainment unit. Or squeeze in a walk to work by getting off at an earlier train or bus stop, or parking a little further from your workplace. Even doing 15 minutes of exercise is better than nothing, so work to create an environment that supports active living.

CAN A CROP TOP CHANGE SOMEONE'S LIFE?

To be honest, I never thought it could. But over the years I've met countless women who have told me that a Lorna Jane crop top or inspirational singlet provided them with their motivation to lose weight, move their body and ultimately change their life.

We were celebrating the opening of our 100th store recently when a woman tapped me on the shoulder and said, "Excuse me, I just wanted to let you know that your crop tops changed my life." It was Sheridan Wright, a contestant from *The Biggest Loser*. When she started out on her weight loss journey she was 136kg, and she told me that fitting into a pair of Lorna Jane leggings and a crop top was one of her ultimate goals.

And then there is Bec Watson, who works with us in Sydney. She was a customer of ours but initially, she couldn't fit many of our styles. That didn't stop her from buying a few outfits and keeping them at home as her inspiration. Bec went on to lose 60kg, almost half of her body weight, and even though she says Lorna Jane was her inspiration, hearing Bec's story and what she's achieved is a huge inspiration to me.

FASHION IS FUEL

Think of the fun rituals we go through when we're preparing for a beautiful event. What if we put the same sort of excitement and ritual behind getting ready to exercise? Wouldn't it become so much more enjoyable? We can wear flattering, comfortable clothes that make us feel good, stack our iPod with upbeat, invigorating songs, grab a bottle of water and get going. By creating a positive, enjoyable ritual, being active becomes something we look forward to. Suddenly, fashion is fuelling your journey, just as much as being active helps you to look good in fashion.

"I still remember how it felt when I finally went to Lorna Jane and tried on a size 12 crop top and it fit."

SHERIDAN'S STORY

Before Lorna Jane

In 2007, I stepped on the scales and my weight was 136kg. I remember thinking, "How did I get here?" I had applied for the second series of *The Biggest Loser* and when I didn't get in, I was heartbroken. Over the next 12 months I lost 16kg but I was still 120kg, so when *The Biggest Loser* opened auditions for series three, I tried again.

I laid myself bare and said, "I'm dreadfully unhappy and I'm lonely. I want to have a partner and have children and be healthy but I don't think these things are going to happen unless I make dramatic changes." I got in! It was fantastic but I left the show relatively early after losing 20kg. When I came out I had an amazing trainer, Lucy, and within three months I reached my goal weight of 75kg.

When I was bigger, I couldn't shop for clothes in regular stores, which is something most people take for granted. For me, walking into a Lorna Jane store to buy work-out gear was on my list of goals. I had been looking forward to it and on the days when I was feeling unmotivated, I would think, "I want to fit into those freaking Lorna Jane crop tops!"

I still remember how it felt when I finally went to Lorna Jane and tried on a size 12 crop top and it fit. The girls in the shop were lovely and I felt like a million dollars.

BEC'S STORY

As a teenager, I was an elite athlete for synchronised swimming. I spent my teen years training and living an active life, but when I stopped competing, I kept eating as though I was. The weight crept on slowly and I didn't really notice it – or didn't want to notice it – instead busying myself in work and studies.

In January 2008 I needed a shoulder reconstruction and I was told I'd never be able to swim again, or lift more than 5kg, or hang washing on the line. I was only 30 years old. I had to take back control of my life and be healthy again, so over the next 22 months, I concentrated on my exercise and nutrition. I lost a total of 60kg and well and truly reclaimed an active and healthy lifestyle.

When I started exercising, I wanted to cover up and hide from everyone in the gym. But as the weight dropped my confidence grew and I realised that how I felt when I exercised impacted my actions.

I'd gotten into the pattern of accepting that there were only certain clothes I could wear but suddenly a whole new wardrobe opened up to me. I went into Lorna Jane and the girls in the store were so helpful and genuine in wanting to find things that suited me. I immediately loved how the clothes felt and looked – feminine, fashionable and functional – and that was the start of my love affair with Lorna Jane!

On one of my shopping trips, I talked about my weight loss with the Lorna Jane girls and they were so affirming of my life choices, I couldn't help but feel that they truly believed in living an active lifestyle too. In January 2011, I applied for a casual position and have been working at Lorna Jane ever since. I love it, I get to meet a variety of people and I love encouraging them that wherever they are in life, it's possible to grasp life with both hands.

Before Lorna Jane

"I had to take back control of my life and be healthy again, so over the next 22 months, I concentrated on my exercise and nutrition."

YOU ARE THE **ONE** THAT CAN **STRETCH** YOUR **HORIZON.**

- EDGAR F MAGNIN

LOYAL LORNA JANE CUSTOMERS AND THEIR JOURNEYS

One of the most surprising and rewarding words I've heard people use to describe the Lorna Jane range is "addictive". One of our wonderful customers recently wrote on our Facebook page, "Going to the gym is easier when you love, and are comfortable, with what you're wearing. I'm addicted to Lorna Jane."

For me, there's no higher compliment. I design activewear with the aim of motivating women to get moving in garments that look as good as they feel and when that concept clicks with someone, it gives me such a sense of satisfaction. I feel the women who wear Lorna Jane are part of our "sisterhood" and by wearing our brand, they're declaring to the world that they value health, fitness and vitality.

Being fortunate enough to meet and interact with many of our customers, I'm always struck by how positive and inspiring they are. It's one of the best parts of my job because I get to see exactly how much of an impact my *Move, Nourish, Believe* philosophy can have.

When I hear about some of the incredible goals our Lorna Jane customers have achieved, I feel humbled and honoured to have been a part of their journey. Like Samantha, a 40-year-old mother of three who not only lost weight, but who transformed her entire body and is now getting ready to compete in bodybuilding competitions. Or Lynn, who once weighed over 100kg and, after dropping more than 40kg, gave up her successful corporate job to launch a new career in personal training.

For these women, Lorna Jane clothing was often the inspiration that helped them achieve their weight loss goals. They were determined to fit into one of our crop tops or a pair of our tights and they put in the hard yards to reach their goals. When I see how much they have achieved, I am truly awe-struck and it makes me even more determined to create better products and provide greater inspiration to support our amazing Lorna Jane customers in the future.

Before Lorna Jane

SAMANTHA SWALLING

"I was determined to achieve my goals"

My name is Samantha and I am 40 years old. I am married to Dean. I am a mother of three children – Felicity 22, Jessica 19 and Zac 12. I'm also a grandmother to baby Scarlette (Felicity is her mummy).

I decided on 30th November 2009 that I needed to lose the kilos and get healthy. It has opened up a whole new world for me. I love it and love who I've become.

Never in my life had I done any form of sport or fitness. Always very quiet with no confidence, I am now building that confidence in myself.

I started walking around my local area which is very hilly. I would do a 5km route at least five nights a week. I knew the basics of changing my diet so when I committed to that I certainly saw results. My starting weight was 67kg and I am 152cm tall.

I decided the gym was my next step. I was overwhelmed with all the fit looking people around but I was determined to achieve my goals. My husband was, and is, so supportive,

he's awesome. Twelve months in the gym doing every class possible was working, but I had a bigger goal. I wanted to build muscle and needed to find a gym that specialised in weight training. I've since changed gyms and have a well known and highly respected personal trainer in the bodybuilding world. She is a former competitor and also loves Lorna Jane. I am well on my way to achieving my goals and building lean muscle with the brilliant expertise and advice from my trainer. I have decided to compete next year.

I look at my before and after photos and am very proud. This experience has been life-changing and I love my new way of life.

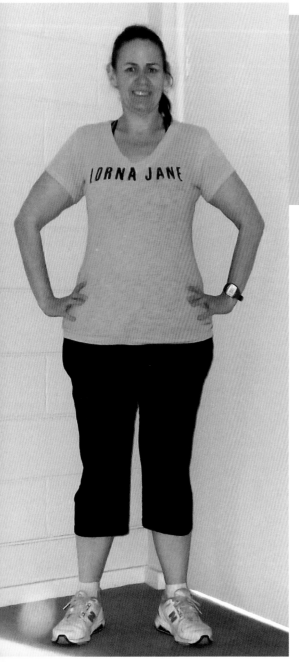

Before Lorna Jane

KARYN'S FAVOURITES
LJ clothing: Mandy Tee, fits perfectly and I can move so easily in it
Move: Rowing and stair climbing
Nourish: Banana smeared with natural peanut butter; protein and carbs.
Weight loss: 83.3kg

Motto you live by: Be your own inspiration

KARYN COLEY

I have lost 83.3 kilos over the past five years. I have done this through healthy eating and exercise. I train with my trainer three times a week.

In the beginning I didn't feel I belonged at the gym. Slowly over time I realised not only did I belong but I deserved to be there. Initially, I was very unfit and in most sessions I would have at least one dizzy spell.

Now I do back to back fitness classes and part of my cardio exercise, which I do by myself, is to climb 35 flights of stairs and I no longer get dizzy spells. I have not finished my journey yet though, I still have nearly 18kg to lose. I want to eventually be able to enter in 5km runs and be able to do burpees and push-ups with perfect form.

And of course being able to wear fashionable clothes from Lorna Jane that I can fit into and feel good in is an added bonus! My life has gone from the boring work, eat and sleep routine to a fit, active lifestyle - and things can only get better from here.

"In the beginning I didn't feel I belonged at the gym. Slowly over time I realised not only did I belong but I deserved to be there."

I wasn't always a "freaky fitness type". Weighing over 100kg and spending most of my time "climbing the corporate ladder", I was not the only one who literally laughed out loud when my name was announced as the winner of a V Club gym membership at a staff function.

I spent the first few weeks laughing the prize off as a joke but when the announcement was printed in the newsletter, more and more of my colleagues started suggesting that I make the most of it.

I decided under peer pressure to give it a go and after 12 months of sweating, moving (a lot) and eating right... I lost over 40kg. When things got tough I just remembered Lorna's philosophy of move, nourish, believe and that kept me going.

Following my success, my friends, family and colleagues continually ask me for tips and suggestions about how to manage the work/life balance with their health. I got such a buzz out of helping people and finding ways to make it work for them... that I studied at the Australian Institute of Fitness, gave up a successful corporate office gig and started Kickstart PT.

The rest (and me at over 100kg) is history.

LYNNE'S FAVOURITES
LJ clothing: Elsy Long Sleeve Hoodie
Move: Boxing
Nourish: Water
Weight loss: 45kg

Motto you live by: Every journey begins with a single step - you'll never finish if you don't start

LYNNE WELCH

Before Lorna Jane

I went to the doctor feeling really unwell with constant pains in my chest. He sent me off to a cardiologist who then told me at 103kg I was at risk of having a heart attack, my blood pressure was sky high - 210/140 - and I had a leaky heart valve. I went home worrying myself and my family sick.

Over the next few weeks I tried to lose weight and couldn't do another fad diet, I made a couple of phone calls and decided an all ladies gym would suit me. So, in July 2010, off I went to Contours Merrylands, NSW and met

a great bunch of trainers. They guided me through the next 12 months with training and weight loss ideas for great meals.

To date I still attend the gym as often as possible and weigh 73kg, a total loss of 30kg, and feel fantastic. The trainers there are amazing. Hard work and motivation is the key to success.

Before Lorna Jane

APRILE WOOLCOCK

APRILE'S FAVOURITES
LJ clothing: Mandy Tees
Move: Boxing
Nourish: Roast vegetable pasta bake
Weight loss: 30kg

Motto you live by: Never give up, giving up is not an option.

"Hard work and motivation is the key to success"

Before Lorna Jane

NAT REYNOLDS

My journey to become fit and healthy always seemed to be never-ending, losing some weight, putting it back on, the cycle would go on forever. In 2009, when my second child was about six months old, I was over 110kg, struggling to walk because my hips, knees and especially my ankles couldn't handle my weight. I decided I needed to seriously do something or how else was I going to keep up with my two kids.

After losing some of the weight I finally got the courage up to get back to the gym, still self-conscious about how I looked but determined to not let it get to me.

It was going to the gym that really opened my eyes to the world of Lorna Jane and I was determined that one day I'd be able to wear something, anything from Lorna Jane and be comfortable and look great.

So that was my goal. I worked hard sorting out my diet and exercise. It's difficult to find the perfect balance to fit in a healthy lifestyle with work and family and allowing time for yourself. For me I found the balance by creating an extra hour or so in my day and working out at 5:30am up to six times a week.

It took a while but I got there and I lost over 20kg. Then I decided to go in and just try on a pair of tights at Lorna Jane and see how close I was, turns out I was closer than I thought and I walked out with no fewer than four items.

I now weigh 74kg (a size 10 or 12) and the only thing that is getting bigger is my collection of Lorna Jane. Though some of my original purchases will have to be culled soon as they are too big, what a shame I'll have to go shopping for more.

Before Lorna Jane

DONNA LOW

DONNA'S FAVOURITES
LJ clothing: Inspirational singlets
Move: Running
Nourish: Fruit, especially strawberries
Weight loss: 42kg

Motto you live by: Never, ever, ever give up!

old, I knew this time it was for me and this time it was for life. I knew what to do, I knew how it worked, I knew I could do it myself and as I had two small children I decided to join as an online member. I didn't mind how long it took to lose the weight because it was coming off for good!

As a reward I bought a Pandora bracelet and for every 5kg I lost I rewarded myself with a charm to go on the bracelet.

I have never, ever been able to run; I was always last in school races. Last year I purchased a "C25k" (couch to 5km) iPhone app and taught myself to run in nine weeks. I have since completed a 5km, 8km and 10km fun run.

I have learnt that I can do anything I set my mind to. I love the Lorna Jane motto Move, Nourish, Believe. Prior to December 2010 I had never set foot inside a Lorna Jane store, now I could spend all day there! I love how her activewear makes you feel fantastic and how the inspiring, motivating quotes make you want to "never, never, never give up!"

I am now a Weight Watchers "Healthy Life Awards" entrant for 2011 and I love my new life.

Having been overweight since my teenage years, my dress sizes went up as my age did - size 14 at 14, size 16 at 16, size 18 at 18 and size 20 at 20 - I decided to join Weight Watchers at the beginning of 2000 and lost 54kg. However when I met my husband I put the weight back on. My weight went up and down following the birth of my son and daughter (now 5 and 2 years old).

I joined Weight Watchers, for the fourth time, in July 2009, when my daughter was only 6 weeks

THE **DIFFERENCE** BETWEEN TRY AND **TRIUMPH** IS A LITTLE **UMPH.**

- MARVIN PHILLIPS

THE FIT WOMAN'S SECRET

Lorna Jane and her loyal customers share their secret weapons for sneaking an extra boost of energy and movement into their day.

Lorna Jane: I must use the stairs, even if there's an escalator available... at airports, in offices, at shopping centres, wherever I am, if I'm given the opportunity to use stairs, I'll take them. It's my "unwritten rule" and it helps me sneak in that extra bit of movement every day. You'll find that if you make an effort to do this at every opportunity, it will quickly become an unconscious habit.

Rachel Orr: I purposely run up and down the stairs at work when I don't need to, and carry small amounts of stuff so I have to do several more trips up and down them.

Katherine Ma: Lunges and squats while trying to rock a baby to sleep.

Skye Accatino: I do sit-ups using my baby as the weight on my chest (she laughs the whole time).

Amy Simpson: I do calf raises whenever I'm at the photocopier or scanner, while cutting up veggies or washing the dishes. I also do butt squeezes when on the phone or at traffic lights.

Rachel O'Grady Chrichton: Jump around in a bouncy castle with my children. It's amazing for your gluts and quads.

Jaimee Brian: Belly dancing while brushing my teeth... feel the burn.

Mietta Reynolds: Doing squats after a shower while blow-drying my hair.

Nat Turner: Would have to be sexercise. We all know the saying. Just do it.

TIPS FOR EXERCISING WHEN YOU ARE TRAVELLING

BE REALISTIC: When I travel my goal is to stay active for the entire trip but I am realistic; sometimes it's just not possible. I set down the rules from the beginning – such as, don't skip training more than one day in a row – to make myself accountable.

HAVE A PLAN: Planning is paramount to success in all areas of life. I plan my packing, making sure I include outfits that look good with running shoes, so I can wear them all day and not just for my work-out. This way I am encouraged to move more during the day.

WALK: When you're on holiday you tend to do a lot of walking, which is great exercise in itself. I love to walk, it's a great way to explore your destination and clear your head after being cooped up in a plane. A good walk gets your circulation going and leaves you feeling refreshed.

EXPLORE GRAB-N-GO: When I get to my destination I grab the business card of the hotel where I'm staying and head out to explore. I get my bearings by meandering through the local streets and check out cafes and shops I'd like to revisit. I don't necessarily stay close to the hotel because I can always hop in a taxi if I get lost – that's what the business card is for.

BECOME A LOCAL: Find a local gym or studio so you can do a casual class and chat to the people you meet. You might develop some friendships and almost certainly obtain some inside information on the places only locals would know about.

ABIDE BY THE UNWRITTEN RULE: Travelling is the perfect opportunity to put my "unwritten rule" into practice. That means not using the escalators or lift if there are stairs available. It makes for a good cardio workout if you're staying on the 15th floor of a hotel.

BOOK SMART: I always book hotels that have a fitness centre. If I've got jetlag I can get on the treadmill right away and shake it off. It also gives me an opportunity to squeeze in some exercise in the gym if I don't get a chance to be active during the day.

GET INVOLVED: Wherever I am, I get involved in the local culture. When you are booking your next holiday, google active things to do. Are there any great hikes or bike tracks? Are there adventure companies where you can learn something new, like paddleboarding or surfing? Who knows, you might even discover a new way to move that you can bring back home with you.

LAY IT OUT: I still lay out my clothes every evening so that I wake up the next morning feeling motivated to do some kind of activity – it's a ritual that I take everywhere with me.

NO BED AND BREAKFASTS: I try to avoid booking hotel rooms where breakfast is included in the rate, as it means I feel the pressure to get up, exercise and be back at the hotel so I don't miss the cut-off time for breakfast. I prefer to wake up naturally and workout without the pressure of time constrictions and then finish with a brisk walk to a local café for breakfast.

IF WE ALL DID THE THINGS WE ARE CAPABLE OF DOING WE WOULD LITERALLY ASTOUND OURSELVES.

– THOMAS EDISON

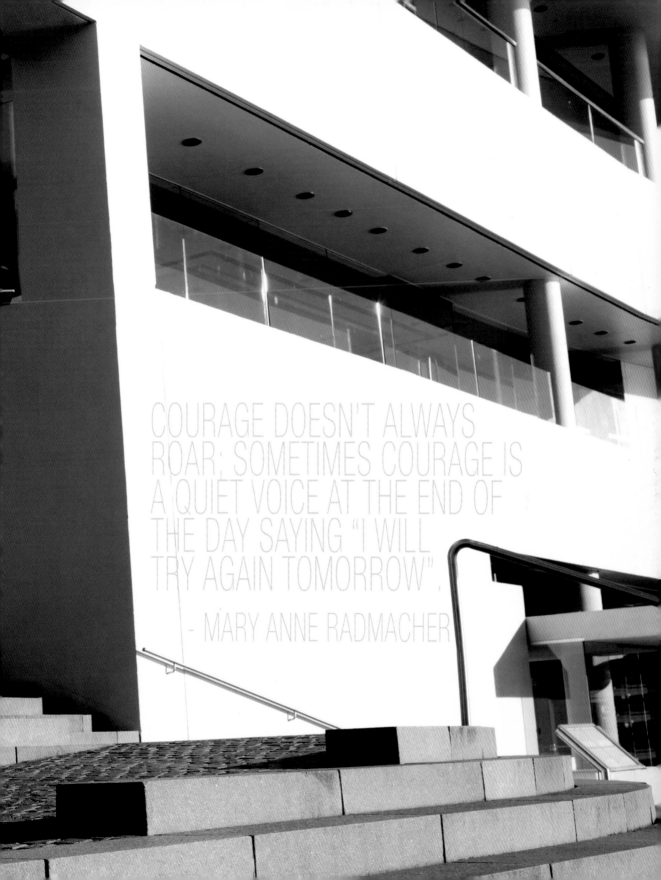

COURAGE DOESN'T ALWAYS ROAR; SOMETIMES COURAGE IS A QUIET VOICE AT THE END OF THE DAY SAYING "I WILL TRY AGAIN TOMORROW".

- MARY ANNE RADMACHER

FITNESS TRENDS

In the fashion industry there's only one constant, and that is change. I launched Lorna Jane in 1990 and in the two decades since, I have seen virtually every trend come and go. From leotards to spin shorts, fluoro colours to classic black and oversized sweats to snug, body-fitting tees – when it comes to the ever changing, ever fickle world of fashion, I've seen it all.

When I first began designing activewear all those years ago, the fashion palette was bold and bright. Women weren't afraid to wear neon hues and clashing patterns. The look of the moment was coloured or black tights paired with a top or leotard and really thick slouch socks and chunky sneakers.

By the mid 90s, we were experimenting with a whole new style – remember the safety pin dress that Elizabeth Hurley wore to the Oscar's in 1994? Huge panels had been cut out from each side of the dress, which was held together by oversized safety pins. It was such a bold statement from designer Gianni Versace and it wasn't long before that trend was sweeping through the fashion industry.

I almost cringe remembering my take on this trend and it makes me laugh now, but at the time it was so popular and sold out repeatedly for two collections. We even received a fashion award for it.

It's been a crazy ride but I am proud that Lorna Jane has been able to evolve and stay connected with its customers through the changing fashion environment. These days, we produce a core range of activewear that is available year round, but we also create a collection of 70 to 100 new designs every single month. I think because of this, we feel even more pressure to stay on top of the latest fashion trends. It's not always easy, I have to admit, but it's a challenge I enjoy tackling month-in, month-out.

1980s: Muscle mania was in full swing with Mr and Mrs Universe competitions and Muscle & Fitness magazine culture influencing the way we "created" our bodies. Fluro, lycra g-string leotards were as sought after as they were high-cut – a statement look that swept through the nation, thanks to Olivia Newton-John as she inspired us all to "Get Physical". Every woman wanted to be Olivia and I found myself under the wrath of a ballet teacher who was furious at me for chopping my hair off ONJ-style a few days before my ballet recital.

Early 1990s: The first Lorna Jane store opened in Brisbane, Australia as women demanded made-to-measure pieces to express themselves whilst they high leg-kicked their way into shape. The aerobics class reigned supreme and cardio addicts relished in the gut-busting workouts that had you sweating for a solid hour. If you weren't in a class, you were part of the road-running craze, sporting lightweight running shorts and an over-sized t-shirt that brought out the Forrest Gump in us all.

Mid 1990s: Designed for the fearless, swimsuits and leotards with "dare to bare" cutouts became a prominent fashion trend, and I jumped right on the bandwagon with my famous Swiss Cheese swimsuit that took the gong at the eponymous 1994 Retailers Association of Queensland (RAQ) awards. With the glass ceiling beginning to crack under the pressure of women in business becoming power players, exercise habits evolved. In their drive to fit exercise in around a busy schedule, independent exercise routines were embraced and gyms full of cardio machines popped up faster than you could say "treadmill".

Late 1990s: Women wore skorts and sweatpants, and revealing the midriff became the must-do fashion statement. Block colours reigned supreme and capri cropped pants and low-waisted styles also made their way into every woman's casual and activewear rotation. With the low-fat craze in full swing, women were trying every gimmick possible to ditch the kilos, including experimenting with ab-rollers and air-walkers.

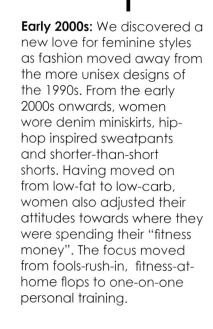

Early 2000s: We discovered a new love for feminine styles as fashion moved away from the more unisex designs of the 1990s. From the early 2000s onwards, women wore denim miniskirts, hip-hop inspired sweatpants and shorter-than-short shorts. Having moved on from low-fat to low-carb, women also adjusted their attitudes towards where they were spending their "fitness money". The focus moved from fools-rush-in, fitness-at-home flops to one-on-one personal training.

Mid 2000s: By this stage, the low-rise was firmly established as the one and only cut of the modern woman. With yoga becoming increasingly popular and technological advances being made in performance wear, leggings and tights flooded the gyms as women looked for new and interesting ways to get fit. The return of the regular class was met with innovative offerings, which saw Body Attack, Body Balance and Body Pump become workout words in vogue.

Late 2000s: The modern woman began to realise that if she adopted fashion-forward activewear as regular clothing, she could incorporate movement into her daily routine, instead of having the pressure to find an hour every day specifically for exercise. With the pilates class acting as the perfect introduction to core strength awareness, the low impact movement gained popularity and introduced exercise to a whole new group of women inspired to get active. Much emphasis was placed on looking the part and teaming with the theme: print tights with matching crops and headbands completed the perfect activewear look, and women became brave enough to move into bold colours like red, pink and yellow while exercising.

MOVE. NOURISH. BELIEVE.

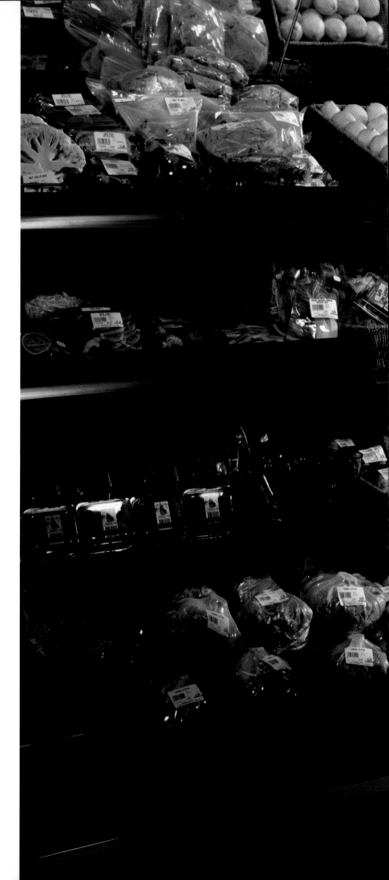

THOU SHOULDST EAT TO LIVE; NOT LIVE TO EAT.
- SOCRATES

Like most women, I pay attention to what I eat, but I'm not one of those people who survive on a diet of leafy greens and fruit. I love good food and there are few things I enjoy more in life than sitting down to a delicious meal.

Sadly, I've noticed that there seems to be something of a disconnect between healthy and tasty food, which probably stems from the western world's addiction to dieting. With such a focus on sacrifice in our diet and restricting our calorie intake to be healthy and slim, we've been conditioned to believe that nutritious food must be boring, repetitious and tasteless. I believe that because a particular food is packed with nutrients, it doesn't mean it can't be incredibly tasty, so I'm going to show you just how delicious healthy food can be.

The bottom line is that good nutrition is essential for good health. It doesn't matter how much you exercise, if your diet is full of fast food, takeaways, pre-packaged meals and processed snacks, you'll never be able to truly nourish your body and give it the energy it needs to think and perform at its best.

"wake up and throw away all your excuses."

As a woman in my 40s I have learned that diets are deceiving. They promise the world and give very little except for disappointment and quite often, they are more depressing than uplifting. The reason I am so passionate about nourishing your body with the food it deserves is because when I made the decision to do this for myself, I was astounded at how much it changed my life.

The moment I gave up focusing on the things I couldn't have and started concentrating on all the delectable things I could have, I began to get excited about each day and the opportunity to create marvelous culinary combinations. More than this, my attitude shift actually enabled me to transform my body and put me in the best shape I have been in years.

A big part of this is making smart choices by eating food that is nutritious, fresh and healthy. I choose to eat seasonally where I can because it's not only healthier and tastier, it's also cheaper and better for the environment. Another great thing about eating seasonally is that it forces you to try new ideas and recipes as the available produce is constantly changing. You don't find yourself eating the same meals day-in day-out and it guarantees you a wider variety of nutrients throughout the year.

Trust me, life isn't about living to a strict diet plan, the best we can do is make good decisions and aim for balance. The way I see it, if 90% of what I eat is nutritious, fresh and local, I'm doing okay.

EIGHT GLASSES A DAY

Water is life's most essential nutrient. It's the most important of the 50-plus nutrients we require on a daily basis and although we can survive up to several weeks without food, we can't live more than three or four days without water. There are some powerful reasons to drink lots of water every day and forming the habit isn't hard with a little focus and commitment.

We all know the golden rule is to drink eight glasses of water a day (and one more for each hour of exercise or air travel). A useful tip to remember is to sip your water rather than gulping it down by the glassful, as it helps prevent you from running to the bathroom every 15 minutes.

Here's how I squeeze my eight glasses in:

Glass #1
I keep it by the bed to drink as soon as I wake up

Glass #2:
I have a glass of water with my daily women's multi-vitamin

Glass #3:
I have one glass with breakfast (more if I have worked out)

Glass #4:
I have this one after my morning coffee when I get to work

Glass #5:
Drink with lunch

Glass #6:
I keep a glass on
my desk to sip
throughout the
afternoon

Glass #7:
Drink with dinner

Glass #8:
I sip before I go
to bed

CAUSE AND EFFECT

When you're young, it can be harder to appreciate the link between cause and effect. Women in their teens and 20s think they can do all sorts of things – skip breakfast, smoke, drink, party, wear their make-up to bed, barely drink any water – and still wake up in the morning with clear skin, shiny hair and a fabulous figure.

The truth of the matter is that, eventually, the way you live your life will catch up to you. It's important to make smart choices that benefit your body from an early age because there is a strong link between what you eat and how you treat your body when you're younger and how you will look and feel as you age.

I'm in my 40s and fortunate to be fit, healthy and full of energy, but it's not pure luck that has led me to this point. When I was growing up my family was health conscious and, as a result, I was mindful of nourishing my body from a young age.

I've come to realise that because I respect my body and give it what it needs, in return it allows me a little leeway on the days that I'm not that good. I rarely eat processed, fatty foods and I maintain a consistent level of fitness, so when I do deviate from my normal healthy routine (cause), I feel less of an impact on my body (effect).

Think of the last time you ate something rich or fatty for lunch, like a greasy fast food meal or a creamy, pasta dish. Do you remember how you felt afterwards? Sluggish? Tired? Bloated?

There's a reason these foods don't make you feel good. Take pasta, for instance. It is made with the same ingredients that are in glue, flour and water. And that's why when you eat pasta for lunch, you can feel weighed down, unproductive and sedentary for the rest of the day. Your body is trying to process this "heavy" food and has no energy for anything else. I'm not saying don't ever eat pasta, but consider your options and be mindful of what will fuel your body in the best way. Also, keep an eye on your portion size and opt for a tomato-based sauce rather than cream.

I've learnt that I need to fuel my body to perform at its best every day and I usually opt for healthier alternatives at lunch – such as a mixed salad with protein, a salad wrap, or a nutritious soup. They are just as delicious, won't slow me down, and give me the brain fuel I need for the rest of my day.

TO EAT IS A NEC EAT INTELLIGEN

- FRANCOIS DE LA RO

ESSITY, BUT TO
LY IS AN ART.

EFOUCAULD

I CAN ACHIEVE ANYTHING WHEN I'VE GOT A PLAN

One of my all-time favourite mantras is, "I can achieve anything when I've got a plan". I use it in all areas of my life and especially when it comes to nutrition. My philosophy is, why make a dozen different decisions every day about what you're going to eat when you could make one decision per week?

If you don't have a plan, it can be harder to resist temptation. For instance, you might get to work and someone has brought in a cake to celebrate their birthday. The cake comes out at around 11am, and although you have a delicious chicken sandwich stashed in the fridge for lunch, that cake looks mighty tasty. Surely a small piece wouldn't hurt, would it?

On its own, probably not, but what about the hot chocolate you treated yourself to on the way to work? And the Thai takeaway you're going to order tonight because you'll be working late and by the time you get home, you'll be too tired to cook?

The alternative is to set yourself up with a framework to follow, so you can stay on track. Start by creating a plan for your main meals and snacks for the week. I'm not saying you actually have to make all the food in one sitting but instead map out a guide to your weekly food choices. And please don't confuse being organised with being boring. It's not about restricting yourself, but about making good decisions and creating positive rituals that encourage you to eat well. It's also a great way to make sure you include a wider variety of nutritious food in your weekly diet and makes shopping so much quicker and easier.

If you love getting a coffee on your commute to and from work, you can still do that, but start to tweak your order. If you ordinarily order two full-fat lattes a day with two sugars, try them with skim milk. Then substitute white sugar for raw sugar. Then cut back from two sugars to one and, eventually no sugar at all.

You have to choose what is important to you and for some people, coffee is a non-negotiable part of the day. For others, it's having a sweet treat after dinner each night. Whatever it is, find a way to make healthier food choices work within the parameters of your own life. Ultimately, it boils down to making conscious decisions about what you want to put into your body, what you can live without and what you can't. But I guarantee you this – when you make positive changes in your diet and you realise what nutrients can do for you, the results are amazing.

NUTRITIONAL FACTS

Food can play an important role in boosting your immune system and minimising the aging process. There are so many superfoods that we can incorporate into our diets to keep us looking and feeling younger and more energised:

Bananas contain vitamin B6, which helps your body fight infection.

Beetroot supports your liver by helping it cleanse the blood of impurities.

Pure unsweetened coconut water is one of the most hydrating fluids you can drink. Its isotonic solution is almost identical to blood plasma, so it keeps your cells plump and hydrated and gives you glowing skin.

Spinach is loaded with vitamin K, which protects against osteoporosis.

The Guinness Book of Records lists avocados as the most nutritious fruit in the world.

Allicin, one of the active components in freshly crushed garlic, can kill off viruses by blocking the enzymes that lead to infection.

Increase your iron absorption by eating iron-rich foods in conjunction with vitamin C. So try eating your steak with a glass of orange juice.

Bananas

beetroot

coconut water

Spinach

avocados

Garlic

Sprinkle cayenne pepper on soup when you have a cold. Its active ingredient, capsaicin, beats congestion by thinning the mucus in your nasal passages, so you can breathe freely again.

The antioxidants in tea provide biomarkers in our blood, which help protect us from the damaging effects of oxidation and aging.

I find peppermint tea refreshing and I also like lemon and ginger for their digestive properties.

Asparagus is rich in glutathione, which is our body's most powerful antioxidant.

If I'm feeling under the weather, I take olive leaf extract for an instant antioxidant injection. It helps fight colds, flus and viral infections. It's also been proven by researchers to lower blood pressure and increase blood flow by relaxing the arteries.

EATING WELL -
WHEREVER YOU ARE

Eating well at home is one thing, but it's a different story when you're out at a restaurant, at a friend's house or travelling. It's easier to fall into bad eating habits when you're on the go, so here are my tips for staying healthy when you're not totally in control of the menu.

Fill up beforehand: If you're going to a party or event where you know the food won't be healthy make sure you eat before you go. Tell other people you've already eaten, so they don't think you're antisocial and you won't be subconsciously tempted to snack on high-calorie party foods.

Skip to the main: At a restaurant, skip the bread and entrée and go straight to the main. I usually choose protein like steak or fish with green vegetables and I ask for any sauces to be served on the side.

Sweet treats: I love eating dessert so when I'm at a restaurant with Bill, I usually steal a couple of teaspoons of his dessert instead of ordering my own. I know it's the first few mouthfuls that taste the best, so by sharing it I get to enjoy the sweetness without loading up on all the calories.

Don't get too hungry: When you get to the point where you're starving, it's hard to stop yourself from just grabbing anything to eat. You'll be more likely to make bad decisions, so don't let yourself reach that point in the first place by always carrying healthy snacks in your purse.

Pre-order: When you're catching a flight, pre-order a low-fat meal with your airline at least 48 hours before you take off. Pack healthy snacks like almonds or a grainy muesli bar to avoid ordering from in-flight snack menus. I also take some protein powder on longer flights and a couple of pieces of fruit (but be mindful of dumping any leftovers before you go through customs – food products are not what you want them to find in your bag!)

Keep hydrated: Drinking a couple of litres of water is a good habit to have anyway but it becomes even more important when you're travelling. On holidays, take a drink bottle with you and refill it whenever you get the chance. Sipping (rather than drinking a glass at a time) is crucial here because constantly searching for a toilet will certainly dampen your holiday fun. Be sure to avoid sugary, processed soft drinks, as they'll dehydrate you even further.

NOURISH YOUR SPIRIT

Nourishing yourself is about more than just eating the right meals and fuelling your body with fresh, nutrient-rich food. It's also about taking care of your spirit and giving yourself permission to do the things that make you feel happy. As women, our lives are so often consumed by the wellbeing of those around us, particularly family, and sometimes that means our own needs can be swept aside.

In your own life, how much time do you spend doing things you absolutely *love*? When did you last lounge on the sofa with a good book for a couple of hours? Or walk your dog along the beach, feeling the warm sand between your toes? Or relax into a delicious hot bath as the tension of a long day slips away?

Everyone has a different idea of how they like to spend their "me time" but whatever it is that gets your juices flowing, I think it's important to dedicate some of your waking hours to activities that nourish your spirit.

It's easy to say this, but how do you actually achieve it? For me, waking up at 5am every day gives me the opportunity to have an hour or two to myself. I use this time to do the things I love, like reading a good book, playing with my dog or watching a morning TV show. The best way to achieve this in your own life is by creating the environment for it to happen.

For instance, reading is one of my passions so I've created several areas in my home where I can relax with a book. I have a beautiful armchair in my dressing room and there is always a book on the table next to it. I see the book when I get dressed each morning and it's a visual reminder that I'd like to find some time to read that day. If I kept all my books stashed away on a bookshelf, I wouldn't read nearly as much as I do.

As well as creating specific areas in your house, I find it helps to create certain rituals. Since it is as important to nourish your spirit as it is your body, think about ways you can schedule some "me time" into your week. Put it in the diary if you have to, but set aside those times and rituals and do whatever it takes to make it happen.

"I lose my breath, I find my answers."

DON'T FORGET YOUR SKIN

Obviously I'm a big advocate of putting healthy, nutritious things into my body, so as well as eating fresh, healthy foods, I like to use natural beauty products.

Consider this: your skin is your largest organ and it absorbs what you put on it each day, in addition to weathering the elements of everyday life. You need to make it your business to "know" what is in the skincare products you use; ensure they are as natural as possible and free of alcohol and harsh chemicals.

In saying that, I love how my face feels after a facial and how a good quality moisturiser feels on my body but I know first and foremost that good skin starts with good nutrition, so that is where I focus the majority of my time and energy, and I hope you will too.

IT'S NOT ABO
YOU'RE GIVIN
BUT WHAT
YOU'RE GOIN

JT WHAT
G UP,

G TO GAIN.

THE LORNA JANE DIET

My daily diet is healthy but it's also delicious. I look forward to every meal and definitely don't feel like I go without. I'd love all of you to take the challenge and eat how I eat for a week or two. I guarantee, you'll be surprised about how wonderful you feel.

Before you begin, I'd like to point out that when you're starting out with a new healthy eating regime, you'll be more successful if you concentrate on what you're gaining rather that what you're giving up. This was the attitude I adopted when I started drinking my coffee black. It was really hard initially because my morning skinny latte with chocolate on top was almost a religion. To begin with I drank black coffee all week and then treated myself to a skinny latte on the weekends. After a few weeks I found myself preferring black coffee on the weekend too and these days I rarely choose a milk coffee. Interestingly, drinking black coffee has actually made me appreciate good coffee even more as the flavour (and the barista's skills) aren't masked by milk (or chocolate).

Initially it may take hard work to change your mindset and attitude towards food but eventually it becomes second nature. When the positive benefits of eating well start to flow through all areas of your life – from weight loss and reduced bloating to increased energy and clearer skin – you'll start to wonder how you lived any other way.

I like knowing what's in the food I eat, so I avoid overly processed foods and normally bring homemade meals and snacks to work. Here's how I plan my week:

- Weekdays are designated into two healthy days and three diet days (on diet days I basically eat fewer carbohydrates)
- Weekends are classed as healthy days and I incorporate some treats – a favourite is raspberries dipped in dark chocolate for dessert.

I start every day by eating oats combined with a superfood trail mix and natural yoghurt. This is my must-have wake-up meal and I vary it slightly from season to season.

On the weekend I like to go out for breakfast. I'll usually order poached eggs on toast or a vegetarian omelette. What people find interesting is that even when I am planning to go out for breakfast, I still have a protein shake or a smaller version of my oats when I wake up. I need to eat as soon as I get up as I really feel it helps kickstart my metabolism and certainly gives me the energy I need for my morning work-out.

Lunch and dinner will always consist of some sort of protein, whether it's chicken, fish, lamb, or beef, with salad or vegetables. I make my salads interesting by varying the ingredients daily and using plenty of fresh herbs. I'll eat yummy, filling snacks like spiced date slice (page 144) or butternut pumpkin and ginger omelette (page 146) to keep me going through the mornings and afternoons.

I have a sweet tooth so to finish the day, I like to nibble on something for dessert, such as passionfruit and apple crumble (page 143) poached pears (page 135), homemade ice-cream (page 119), or a couple of squares of good quality dark chocolate.

TEN HEALTHY EATING TIPS TO LOOK AND FEEL YOUR BEST

ONE

Use smaller plates

You won't be able to pile as much food onto your plate, so this is a quick, easy way to reduce your portion size. I use this rule for my breakfast oats and dessert. For lunch and dinner, I use a regular sized plate but I make sure I fill it predominantly with salad or vegetables. This way I finish my meal satisfied and don't go searching for more food 30 minutes after I've eaten.

TWO

Eat breakfast

Every day. No exceptions. Everyone knows not to skip meals but they still do it. Skipping meals forces your body into starvation mode, which slows down your metabolism as your body scrambles to preserve energy. It compensates by burning fewer calories than normal and when you do eventually eat again, your body will store those calories (rather than use them) because it expects you to starve it again.

FIVE

Seek out your local farmers market

At a farmers market, farmers from the local area sell their food direct to the public and this means that all produce has been locally grown. They're heaving with fresh, flavourful, seasonal produce and the wholesale prices are a bonus.

SIX

Reduce your carbohydrate intake

I try to have only one carb-based meal a day and it's usually breakfast because I love my oats and need that energy to fuel my morning work-out. For the rest of the day I don't restrict myself too much but I try to keep my carbohydrate portions small.

THREE

Stock up on protein
Protein is the major structural component of every single cell in your body, including organs, muscles, hair and skin, and as a nutrient it is essential for growth and maintenance. So make sure milk, meat, fish, eggs and vegetables are part of your everyday diet.

FOUR

Drink plenty of water
It keeps your skin and body hydrated and reduces your chance of overeating. Aim for eight glasses a day. Try squeezing a little lemon juice in your water, not just for taste but for its alkalising effect on your body.

SEVEN

Meatless Monday
Since officially launching in 2003, this meatless movement sees people all over the world aiming to have one day per week devoid of any meat. Not only is this good for your health and the environment but it's a money saver too.

EIGHT

Don't restrict yourself
If there's a treat you really enjoy, you don't have to give it the flick, just find a way to make it healthier. Replace your daily hot chocolate with a really delicious sweet tea – keep trying all the different herbal teas until you find one you love. If you love ice-cream, make a healthier version rather than eating the calorie-rich supermarket option.

NINE

Eat with a teaspoon

I eat virtually all of my desserts with a teaspoon and have done so from an early age. I find eating with a smaller spoon makes it more enjoyable but it also takes longer and actually allows my body to fill up, so you don't get to the end of your meal thinking you're still hungry.

TEN

Eat fewer packaged foods

If you don't know what's in it, then it's safe to say it's not good for you. Here are a few common supermarket ingredients that can actually negatively impact your health:

Sodium nitrite: A preservative found in processed meats like hot dogs, bacon and sausage, it is used to make meats appear red. Studies have shown that it has been linked to cancer. Sodium nitrite is also used to dye fabrics, as an industrial corrosion inhibitor, in metal coatings; and in the manufacture of rubber chemicals.

Flavour Enhancer 621. This is the official name for monosodium glutamate (MSG), which can cause everything from headaches and nausea to chest pains and heart palpitations. It's hiding in everything from potato chips to barbecue sauce to chicken stock.

ONE CANNOT **THINK** WELL, **LOVE** WELL, SLEEP WELL, IF ONE HAS NOT **DINED** WELL.
- VIRGINIA WOLF

RECIPES

WHO SAID EATING HEALTHY ISN'T DELICIOUS?

I'm surprised by the number of people who think that because I eat healthily, I must eat like a bird. Nothing could be further from the truth. Starving yourself and depriving your body of essential nutrients is never a healthy option and goes against my belief that you need to nourish your body as best you can every single day.

I lead a busy, active life and I'm committed to moving my body as part of my *Move, Nourish, Believe* philosophy. I therefore require enough energy to see me through the day. In addition to breakfast, lunch and dinner, I enjoy a couple of hearty snacks throughout the day and usually finish with something sweet for dessert.

When someone moves to a healthier eating plan, they will often focus on the foods they are limiting from their daily diet rather than the tasty meal options they are opening themselves up to. As a result, many people wrongly assume that healthy eating is all about restrictions, tiny portions and feeling hungry all the time. I'm here to tell you that is not the case at all.

Eating nutritious food has so many benefits – from giving you more energy, to helping your brain stay alert and focused. Healthy meals can be equally delicious (if not more so) than their less-healthy counterparts. To demonstrate how yummy healthy food can be, I've opened up my personal pantry to reveal some of the tasty meals Bill and I enjoy on a regular basis. I hope they inspire you to try something new in your kitchen and help you see that there's really no need to sacrifice flavour in the quest to keep your body and mind nourished from the inside out.

"Many people wrongly assume that healthy eating is all about restrictions, tiny portions and feeling hungry all the time. I'm here to tell you that is not the case at all."

FOOD IN SPRING: SEASON OF RENEWAL AND ABUNDANCE

Spring into the season of renewal and cleansing with flavourful foods at their peak taste. Foods that have gone into hiding through the winter are back to liven the detox that the warmer months bring. You can savour fresh salads with baby carrots and sweet corn and snack on a veritable smorgasbord of juicy citrus fruits. So if your diet's in a slump after the cooling season, get back on track with the freshest produce, all in abundance and ready to help nourish your body back into gear.

SPRING - Breakfast

STRAWBERRY CHEER

- 10 strawberries
- 1 cup oats
- 3 tablespoons chia seeds
- 1 blood orange
- 1 Valencia orange
- Natural yoghurt

Combine chia seeds with juice from ½ blood orange and ½ Valencia orange and let sit for 10 minutes. Pour ¾ cup boiling water onto oats, stir and let cool for 5 minutes. Cut remaining orange halves into segments. Squeeze one segment of each into oats. Chop 4 strawberries into cubes and add to chia seed mixture. Place tablespoon of oats into each glass, followed by a layer of orange segments and yoghurt (optional). Chia and strawberry mix follows next and top this with a layer of strawberry slices. Spoon oats over strawberry slices and repeat layering.

Serves 2

SPRING - Lunch

WHITING WITH CORN CAKES AND AVOCADO SALAD

- 8 whiting fillets
- 3 eggs
- 1 ½ tablespoons skim milk
- 1 ½ tablespoons wholemeal flour
- ⅛ teaspoon baking powder
- ¼ teaspoon pink salt
- 1 cup fresh corn kernels
- 1 bunch shallots
- 1 avocado
- 2 tomatoes
- 1 red onion
- 1 lemon
- Olive oil

Whisk eggs and milk together in a bowl. Mix flour, baking powder and pink salt and stir together with eggs and milk. Mix in corn kernels and a handful of finely chopped spring onions. Cover and let rest at room temperature for 15 minutes. Heat olive oil in pan and add one tablespoon of corn mixture at a time. Cook for 4-5 minutes, flipping once until golden. Keep warm. Deseed tomatoes and chop (reserve the tomato seeds for planting!) and finely chop red onion. Mix tomatoes and red onion together with juice from ½ lemon and season. Carefully cut avocado into cubes and toss gently with tomatoes. Season whiting fillets with salt and pepper and cook for 1-2 minutes on each side. To serve place two whiting fillets beside corn cakes and avocado salsa.

Serves 4

SPRING - Dinner

LAMB, LEMON AND ROSE SALAD

- 400 grams lamb backstrap
- 1 ½ lemons
- 1 radish
- 1 organic rose
- Mixed lettuce
- 1 red onion
- 2 tablespoons fresh finely chopped rosemary
- Olive oil
- 1 teaspoon butter

Mix rosemary and juice from 1 lemon together and pour over lamb. Cover and let marinate for 1 hour in refrigerator, turning occasionally. Sauté onions with butter for 2 minutes. Season lamb and add to pan (reserve marinade). Cook for 3-4 minutes each side, turning once. Remove from pan, cover lamb and let rest for a few minutes. Pour marinade into small saucepan, bring to boil and simmer for 1 minute. Remove from heat. Thinly slice radish and gently tear lettuce. Whisk 1 ½ teaspoons olive oil with marinade reduction. Adjust seasoning and spoon dressing over lettuce in serving bowl. Cut lamb into thin slices and place over lettuce. Sprinkle with radish and rose petals.

Serves 2

SPRING - Dessert

PINA COLADA ICE-CREAM

- 1 fresh pineapple
- 400 ml coconut cream
- ½ cup agave syrup
- 2 large eggs

Blend enough pineapple to make 1 ½ cups of pineapple puree. Heat half of the coconut cream in small saucepan until just below boil. Separate eggs and whisk egg yolks with agave syrup until pale and creamy (reserve egg whites for coconut cones). Pour warm coconut cream into egg mixture and stir over double-boiler for 5 minutes. In a separate bowl, mix pineapple puree and remaining coconut cream. Pour warm mixture into pineapple puree mixture and mix all ingredients together. Allow to cool. Churn in ice-cream machine according to manufacturer's instructions or pour into chilled bowl, cover and freeze, stirring mixture every 15 minutes with a whisk to prevent ice crystals forming and to give finer texture.

Makes 1 litre

COCONUT CONES

- 1 tablespoon unsalted butter
- 1 ¼ cup dessicated coconut
- ½ cup sugar
- 2 egg whites

Preheat oven to 175°C. Make a cone shape using a carrot covered with foil if you don't have a cone-shaped utensil. In a food processor, process the coconut until fine. Add the sugar, egg whites and melted butter and process until all combined. Spoon 1 tablespoon of the batter onto baking paper and using a spatula, spread the batter in a thin and even layer to form a circle approximately 14cm in diameter. Bake for 6-8 minutes, or until a light golden colour. Do not overcook. Transfer to bench and carefully remove each biscuit from baking paper. Roll each biscuit around aluminium-foil cone and gently press and seal into cone shape. Let each cone cool for 2 minutes before carefully removing the inside cone. Repeat with the remaining batter. Transfer the cones to a baking sheet lined with wax paper and chill until set. Fill with scoops of ice-cream and serve at once. Store cones in an airtight container at room temperature for up to 2 days.

Makes 10 cones

FOOD IN SUMMER: KEEP IT COOL

When the sun is scorching, it can only mean one thing – light eating – and what better than fresh tomatoes to zest up our salads? Or a filling mango smoothie to rejuvenate us through the day. In the hotter months, we're seasonally spoilt for choice with an abundance of fresh, tasty produce at its peak. Sweet stone fruits including peaches and nectarines, along with melons, mangos and grapes alike, will liven up your meals and tantalise your taste buds.

GRANOLA BARS

- 2 cups rolled oats
- ½ cup quinoa flakes
- ½ cup shredded coconut
- ¾ cup raisins
- ½ cup dried figs
- ½ cup agave syrup
- 1 vanilla bean (or 1 teaspoon pure vanilla extract)
- 2 tablespoons coconut oil
- 3 tablespoons water
- 1 teaspoon fresh ground cinnamon
- Pinch pink salt

Preheat oven to 170°C and line tray with baking paper. Mix oats, quinoa flakes, shredded coconut and salt together. In another bowl combine agave syrup, coconut oil, water and vanilla seeds (or vanilla extract), then add to dry ingredients. Mix until combined. Press mixture into individual bars on baking paper and bake for approximately 20 minutes until golden. Keep in an airtight container.

Serves 12

MANGO AND STRAWBERRY SMOOTHIE

- 1 mango
- 5 strawberries
- ½ cup coconut water
- ½ cup ice

Cut mango into cubes. Blend mango, strawberries and ice together. Add coconut water. Stir and enjoy immediately.

Serves 2

SUMMER - Lunch

CHERRY AND PORK SALAD

- ◦ 1 pork tenderloin (approx. 450 grams)
- ◦ 20 fresh cherries
- ◦ 1 head frisée lettuce
- ◦ 1 tablespoon olive oil
- ◦ Handful sage leaves
- ◦ ½ brown onion
- ◦ 1 ½ teaspoons butter

Preheat oven to 180°C. Finely chop sage leaves and onion. Rub sage and onion into pork. Secure pork with twine to form even roll shape. Place in baking dish and let marinate for 10 minutes. Cover dish with baking paper and place in oven with a tablespoon of water in dish. Bake in oven for 15-20 minutes. Remove from oven, cover, and leave to rest in baking dish for 5 minutes. Cut pork into slices. Halve cherries and remove seed. Strain liquid from pork into a small bowl and whisk with 1 tablespoon of olive oil. Squeeze juice from 4 cherries into dressing. Adjust seasoning. Dress and toss lettuce with remaining cherries (deseeded) and place pork slices on top. Serve immediately with extra dressing on the side.

Serves 2

SUMMER - Dinner

BARE SALMON WITH BROCCOLINI

- 4 salmon fillets (approx. 200grms)
- 2 bunches broccolini
- 2 cups snow peas
- 3 cloves garlic
- 2 large red chillies
- 1 lemon
- Soy sauce

Preheat oven to 190°C. Cut 4 sheets of baking paper into 25cm lengths. Place salmon fillet on one side of paper, squeeze ¼ lemon on top. Fold piece of paper over to make a secure package. Repeat for the remaining salmon fillets. Bake salmon in oven for 10 minutes or until cooked to preference. Steam broccolini and snow peas separately for a couple of minutes until colour has intensified. Keep warm. Finely crush 3 cloves of garlic and chilli (seeds removed); mix a small amount of the crushed garlic and the crushed chilli into the soy sauce and drizzle over salmon.

Serves 4

SUMMER - Dessert

WATERMELON SANDWICH

- ½ watermelon
- 1 cup fresh ricotta
- 1 lime
- Bunch of watercress
- 2 teaspoons finely chopped mint

Mix ricotta, mint, lime juice and lime zest together. To assemble the sandwiches cut watermelon into 1cm thick slices. Lay watercress on top, spread ricotta mixture and place more watercress on top. Cover with another slice of watermelon. Cut into desired sandwich shape and enjoy chilled.

FOOD IN AUTUMN: SWAP OUT THE CALORIE-RICH DISHES

As the weather cools in autumn and the urge to indulge in comforting casseroles and curries hits, there's no reason why you should deny yourself permission to enjoy hearty meals. That's not to say you can't swap out the calorie-rich dishes for healthier versions, however. Take my chicken curry with coriander and coconut relish, for instance. It's tasty, healthy and made with delicious seasonal ingredients, so it's full on flavour and light on kilojoules. Best of all, when you make a big enough batch you can take it for lunch for the next day as well.

FENNEL OMELETTE WITH CHERVIL

- 4 eggs
- 1 medium fennel bulb
- 1 teaspoon olive oil
- ½ teaspoon butter
- 1 tablespoon of chervil

Slice fennel thinly. Sauté in pan for 2 minutes. Remove and set aside. Crack eggs into bowl, season with salt and pepper and beat thoroughly with fork. Heat olive oil and butter in appropriate omelette pan and pour in beaten eggs. Allow egg mixture to set into a thin skin and then push egg away from sides of pan. Cover half the egg mixture with fennel slices. Fold omelette in half to make semi-circle. Cook for a minute or two longer. Serve with extra fennel and fresh chervil. Mushrooms may also be used instead of the fennel.

Serves 2

AUTUMN - Lunch

YOGHURT CHICKEN

- 4 chicken fillets
- 1 cup natural yoghurt
- 1 lemon
- 2 cloves garlic, crushed
- 1 tablespoon soy sauce

Mix yoghurt, lemon juice and soy sauce into a ceramic bowl. Add garlic to yoghurt mixture. Chop chicken into bite-size pieces and marinate in yoghurt mixture for at least two hours in refrigerator. Cook over medium heat in pan for five minutes, flip and cook until tender for another 5-10 minutes. Remove and cover chicken. Reduce remaining liquid in saucepan by half and spoon over chicken. Enjoy with pomegranate and quinoa tabouli.

Serves 4

POMEGRANATE AND QUINOA TABOULI

- ½ cup quinoa
- 1 pomegranate
- 1 ½ cups parsley, finely chopped
- ¼ cup mint, finely chopped
- Juice of 1 lemon

Rinse quinoa thoroughly and place in small saucepan. Add 1 ¼ cups water and cook over medium heat. When it starts to simmer cover and reduce to low heat. Cook until all water has evaporated and quinoa is translucent (10-12 minutes). Place quinoa in bowl and cool. Add pomegranate seeds and herbs. Combine and season with pink salt, very finely ground pepper and lemon juice.

Serves 4

AUTUMN - Dinner

CHICKEN CURRY

- 600 grams chicken thighs
- 1kg tomatoes
- 2 brown onions
- 1 red onion
- 2 tablespoons coriander seeds
- 1 tablespoon cumin seeds
- 1 cinnamon stick
- 1 red bird's eye chilli
- 2 centimetres fresh turmeric
- 4 centimetres fresh ginger
- 2 tablespoons garam masala
- Bunch of coriander
- ¼ cup desiccated coconut
- 1 ½ tablespoons coconut oil
- ½ cup natural yoghurt
- ½ lemon, juiced

Place coriander seeds and cumin seeds in a saucepan over medium heat for 1 minute until fragrant. Remove from heat and grind with a mortar and pestle. Finely chop onion and sauté in large saucepan with coconut oil for 5 minutes. Add the ground coriander, cumin, garam masala, chilli and ginger and stir constantly for 10 seconds. Add tomatoes to saucepan and let thicken for 10 minutes. Stir in ½ cup water, finely grated turmeric and salt to taste. Bring the sauce to boil and add quartered chicken thighs. Stir sauce over chicken, lower heat, cover and simmer until chicken is tender, approximately 20 minutes. Stir in handful of fresh coriander leaves and simmer for 2-3 minutes. Serve with coriander and coconut relish and brown rice.

Serves 4

CORIANDER AND COCONUT RELISH

Combine coconut with yoghurt and leave to marinate in the refrigerator for 45 minutes. Add 1 cup finely chopped coriander (both leaves and stalks) add salt and juice of ½ lemon. Serve chilled.

Serves 4

AUTUMN - Dessert

CINNAMON INFUSED POACHED PEARS WITH CHOCOLATE

- 4 beurré bosc pears
- ½ lemon, juiced
- 1 cinnamon stick
- 2 tablespoon sugar
- 1 cup dark chocolate

Peel pears smoothly and keep stems attached. Place pears horizontally in saucepan, fill with enough water to cover pears. Add sugar, cinnamon stick and lemon juice and simmer gently until the pears are tender (the ripeness of the pears will determine the time). Remove from heat and leave to cool in poaching liquid. To make chocolate leaves, choose a leaf with a glossy top (Brazilian cherry leaves for example, please do not use poisonous foliage!). Melt chocolate in double-boiler. Delicately spread melted chocolate onto leaf with a teaspoon or small brush. Place leaves on baking paper and refrigerate for ½ hour. Carefully pull leaf away from beneath chocolate. Refrigerate until ready to serve. Serve pears with chocolate leaves, remaining melted chocolate and yoghurt.
Serves 4

FOOD IN WINTER:
WHEN IT'S COLD OUTSIDE

Nothing warms you up quite like a hearty homemade soup, such as my delicious leek and pea soup. The fabulous thing about soup is that you can make a huge pot and then freeze it for later. One of my clever friends spends one Sunday a month making three different soups during winter, then she freezes them and alternates flavours for lunch. Of course, just because we're drawn to wholesome, hot meals in winter, doesn't mean we should forget about the fruit that is coming into season. Rhubarb comes into its own in winter, offering a delicious addition to breakfast and dessert.

WINTER - Breakfast

RUSTIC RHUBARB PORRIDGE

- 3 stems rhubarb
- 1 cup oats
- ½ cup almonds soaked in water overnight
- Natural yoghurt
- ½ lemon, juiced
- 1 cinnamon stick
- 1 teaspoon agave syrup

Place rhubarb, lemon juice, cinnamon and ½ cup water in saucepan over medium heat. Cover and simmer until rhubarb is soft. Take off heat and add agave syrup. Place oats in breakfast bowl and stir in 1 ½ cups boiling water. Divide oats and almonds between two breakfast bowls and add natural yoghurt or milk. Top with poached rhubarb.

Serves 2

WINTER - Lunch

LEEK AND PEA SOUP

- 3 leeks
- 7 shallots, sliced
- 600 grams green peas
- 1 litre vegetable or chicken stock
- 1 tablespoon butter

Cut leeks lengthwise into strips. Remove any soil that may be trapped between layers. In a large saucepan sauté shallots and butter for a few minutes. Add sliced leeks to saucepan with ¼ cup stock. Cook over moderate heat for 10 minutes. Add remaining stock. Simmer gently for 5 minutes. Add peas and cook for a minute or two until tender. Remove from heat, allow to cool for 5 minutes and blend.

Serves 4

WINTER - Dinner

LASAGNE WITH BASIL AND LEMON SALAD

- 500 grams beef mince
- 2 brown onions, finely chopped
- 2 cloves garlic
- 1 tablespoon fresh oregano, finely chopped
- 2 tablespoons fresh sage, finely chopped
- 2 bay leaves
- 800 grams tomatoes
- ½ cup red wine
- 2 tablespoons butter
- 1 tablespoon olive oil
- Lasagne sheets
- 75 grams fresh ricotta
- 600 millilitres milk
- 60 grams butter
- 80 grams plain flour
- ¼ teaspoon fresh nutmeg
- Bunch of basil
- Bunch of sorrel
- 1 lemon
- Salt and pepper
- 5 sprigs of thyme

Score tomatoes and place in large bowl. Pour boiling water over tomatoes and let sit for 1-2 minutes until skin starts to come away from flesh. Remove tomatoes from water and leave until cool enough to handle. Peel tomato skin away from flesh. Chop tomatoes and place in large saucepan over medium heat. Reduce tomatoes for approximately 20 minutes or until most of the watery liquid has evaporated, ideally giving you 2 cups of fresh tomato paste. Heat olive oil in pan with finely chopped onion and sauté for 4-5 minutes. Add garlic and beef and sauté for 10 minutes, stirring constantly. Stir in oregano, sage and bay leaf and season with salt and pepper. Add freshly made tomato paste and cook for 2 minutes. Pour ¼ cup wine into pan and simmer for a couple of minutes. Pour remaining wine into saucepan and cook sauce for a further 10 minutes. For béchamel sauce, heat milk gently in saucepan with 1 bay leaf. In another saucepan melt butter and add the flour, stirring constantly. Gradually add ½ cup of warm milk at a time to saucepan, stirring constantly over medium heat. Remove saucepan from heat and add a grating of nutmeg to sauce. Preheat oven to 180˚C. Spoon a layer of beef sauce, then a layer of béchamel sauce into ovenproof dish. Cover with lasagne sheets and repeat layering. Finish with lasagne sheet topped with remaining béchamel sauce and crumbled fresh ricotta. Cover and cook for 20-25 minutes. After 25 minutes remove cover and cook for further 5 minutes. Remove from oven and sprinkle fresh thyme leaves on top. Serve with a mix of fresh basil and sorrel leaves dressed with lemon juice and zest.

Serves 6

WINTER - Dessert

PASSIONFRUIT AND APPLE CRUMBLE

- ½ cup rolled oats
- ½ cup desiccated coconut
- ¼ cup plain flour
- 2 tablespoons sugar
- 2 tablespoons butter
- 4 Granny Smith apples
- 6 passionfruit

Preheat oven to 170°C. Mix flour and oats together and rub in butter with fingers. Stir in coconut and sugar. Press pulp from 4 passionfruit through a fine sieve. Peel and chop apples. Place chopped apples in individual ramekins or similar dish. Divide passionfruit juice amongst ramekins and spoon crumble mixture on top. Bake in oven for approximately 20 minutes until golden. Remove from oven, serve immediately and drizzle with remaining passionfruit pulp.

Serves 4

SNACKS

SPICED DATE SLICE

- 10 fresh dates
- 70 grams whole almonds
- ¾ teaspoon ground cinnamon
- ¼ teaspoon fennel seeds
- ¼ teaspoon finely ground
- Black pepper
- 1 clove

Blend almonds in food processor or crush with a mortar and pestle so there are some small and some large bits. Remove and place in bowl. Deseed dates and blend in food processor or squash with a mortar and pestle until smooth. Mix spices together (ideally freshly ground) and stir into date mixture. Mix half the almond mixture into dates and spread mixture onto baking paper about 1cm thick. Refrigerate for ½ an hour. Remove from fridge. Press and sprinkle remaining almonds on top and cut into desired shape. Keep refrigerated.

Makes 10

SUPER BLISS BALLS

- 7 fresh dates
- ¾ cup fresh almond meal
- ½ cup muscatels
- ¾ cup desiccated coconut
- 2 tablespoons raw cacao powder
- 1 cluster malabar spinach berries

Deseed dates and muscatels; mix together in food processor or with a mortar and pestle. Combine almond meal, ½ coconut and cacao powder in bowl. Mix in fruit and combine well. Form into balls and roll in remaining coconut that has been coloured with malabar spinach berry juice (a little goes a long way). Another deeply coloured juice may be substituted. Keep refrigerated, although they won't last long!

Makes 12

BUTTERNUT PUMPKIN AND GINGER OMELETTE

- 4 eggs
- ½ butternut pumpkin
- 2 centimetre knob of ginger
- ¼ cup pepitas
- 1 teaspoon olive oil

Preheat oven to 180°C. Peel and deseed pumpkin and chop into large cubes. Place pumpkin in baking dish and cover. Cook in oven for 20 minutes until soft and tender. Mash and press through fine sieve. Crack eggs in a bowl and whisk, then add pumpkin and whisk together. Whisk in finely grated ginger. Place butter in small pan over low heat and add mixture. Cook for 10 minutes. Flip, using a plate, and cook on the other side for approximately 10 minutes. Transfer to serving plate and sprinkle with pepitas.

Serves 2

APPLE, GOAT'S CHEESE AND MINT

- Apple
- Fresh goat's cheese
- Mint

Cut apple into 3mm slices laterally to prevent oxidation (the top of the apple serves as a lid keeping apple slices fresh). Spread goat's cheese on apple and top with mint. Enjoy with herbal tea.

YOGHURT WITH TRAIL MIX

- 1 cup almonds
- ½ cup goji berries
- 1 cup walnuts
- ½ cup dried blueberries
- ½ cup pepitas
- ½ cup sunflower seeds
- Natural yoghurt

Combine all dry ingredients and store in an airtight container. Serve desired quantity with yoghurt.

QUICK SNACKS

Miso Soup
Protein Shake
Fruit
Fresh Nuts

DO WHAT YOU HAVE
TO DO TO BE WHAT
YOU WANT TO BE.

MOVE. NOURISH. BELIEVE.

IN THIS WORLD THERE IS NO FORCE EQUAL TO THAT OF A DETERMINED WOMAN.

It's a powerful mantra... and it's one of my favourites. The reason this mantra resonates so strongly with me is that it perfectly sums up my view of the world. I'm an upbeat, positive person – I've always been this way and my mum actually says she can't remember a time when I wasn't smiling. In most of my childhood photos, I've got a grin on my face. I'm not sure why I've always had such an optimistic attitude but I am certain that without it, I wouldn't be where I am today. Life has dealt me many hurdles over the years and what I've discovered is that a strong sense of self-belief is absolutely crucial in order to overcome them.

My personal mantra of *Move, Nourish, Believe* has provided me with the building blocks to create a beautiful life – one that is happy, healthy, balanced and full of energy. I know that I am living my best life and putting forward the best version of myself every day and I want to inspire you to do the same.

The more you immerse yourself in the concept of *Move, Nourish, Believe* and practice it on a daily basis, the more it will become integrated into your consciousness. Before long, you will follow this philosophy subconsciously – and you'll feel better for it.

SO WHAT DO
PLAN TO DO
YOUR ONE W
AND PRECIOU

OU
ITH
D
LIFE?

THE INSPIRATIONAL SINGLET

The Lorna Jane brand is a reflection of me and my optimistic outlook. I began designing the inspirational singlets with this in mind and they have always featured empowering phrases, positive slogans and confidence-boosting words. I wanted to wear them because they gave me energy and motivation to keep going and I wanted to share the infectious nature of their messages.

I was delighted with how much they resonated with the Lorna Jane customer. I was constantly getting feedback that our positive affirmations not only reminded them to push harder in their training sessions but made them feel empowered to take on challenging situations, helped them get through difficult periods in their lives and even inspired them to stay positive when dealing with illness.

I have inspirational words everywhere around me. I collect fortune cookie slips, put pictures with positive mantras up on the walls at work and at home, and I carry a notebook with me so I can jot down my thoughts when inspiration strikes. I guess you could say the ideas for my singlets come from my life, from what inspires me on a personal level. I have to confess, my mum is constantly suggesting phrases to put on my inspirational singlets but I haven't actually got around to using one yet.

Customers send in pictures of themselves to show how our Inspirational Singlets help them in their life.

SETTING YOUR GOALS HIGHER AND HIGHER

So, what's the secret behind reaching your goals and living the dream life you'd always imagined?

The answer is simple: it is all about choices. We make them every day and it's the way that we choose to do certain things in our lives that can have the biggest consequences.

For instance, to me food that doesn't taste delicious is worthless and I don't see the point in wasting calories on a bland, boring meal. I'm also not interested in eating overly processed, high-fat, high-sugar foods that don't put fibre, vitamins, minerals or anything nutritious into my body.

I know many women have the same attitude and yet, when they're feeling vulnerable or run-down or tired, they make decisions that go against that belief system. It only takes small tweaks to change your habits and when you start to think about life a little differently, you'll begin making positive decisions and choices that move you closer towards your goals.

In working out what you are striving to achieve, I'm going to ask you to do yourself a favour and set the bar as high as you possibly can. It doesn't matter what your goal is. It could be to lose weight or get fit, get a new job, start a new career, launch a new business or move overseas. Whatever it is, make sure you reach for the stars and dream as big as your imagination allows.

If I think back to when I first launched Lorna Jane, I didn't go into it planning to build a global company. However, I did believe I could turn my little hobby into a successful business and, at the time, that seemed like a massive achievement. Lorna Jane's phenomenal growth has happened because I was always determined to be better, to constantly improve the product and the brand, and I believed we could achieve bigger things. I continued to move the goal posts, improving a little day by day, and now I almost have to pinch myself when I realise how far we've come.

I'm not suggesting you should set what might seem like unachievable, "pie in the sky" goals at the beginning of your journey but I am urging you not to give yourself permission to aim for mediocrity – which means you'll need to be brutally honest with yourself about what you want out of life.

I can hear you saying, "But I have so far to go, and so much to do – will I ever get there?"

I'm here to tell you that if you work hard enough, absolutely anything is possible. To get to where you want to go, you simply need to commit yourself to the finish line, and then work backwards, setting more realistic goals to celebrate along the way.

If your goal is to run 10km and you have never run more than three minutes on a treadmill, then grab your goal with both hands and break it down. The first milestone you'll tick off your list is when you can run 1km. Celebrate the achievement with something that nourishes your spirit (think a massage or facial or that new dress that is going to look fabulous on you now, rather than a piece of chocolate cake) but never take your eye off the ultimate prize: that 10km run.

Your next goal post might be 2.5km. Then it's 5km, then 7.5km. Celebrate at each of these milestones as you inch closer towards your goal.

Finally, when you achieve your original goal and knock over the 10km run, you can bask in a glow of success and accomplishment as you realise you've made it. Now it's time to move the goal posts once again as you turn your attention to the 20km run, or maybe a brand new goal altogether?

DREAM. BEL

EVE.
ACHIEVE.

PLANNING FOR SUCCESS

At the end of the day, every risk and leap of faith you take in life comes down to planning. Personally, I don't have a "win at all costs" attitude. I won't step over people to get where I want to go. But I do believe that if you want something badly enough, you can work out the steps you need to take to get there. As the Lorna Jane saying goes: *Dream, Believe, Achieve.*

The journey towards making the Lorna Jane brand what it is today hasn't always been smooth sailing but no matter what has been thrown at me, I have always felt like I could cope as long as I had a plan.

People often ask me, how do you keep a positive, determined attitude in the face of challenging circumstances? My answer is always the same: no matter what I'm up against, I can make it work if I have a strategy to get back on top of things. I've always had this approach, both personally and professionally, and it's helped me overcome all sorts of challenging situations.

Try this approach and see how much better it makes you feel about the obstacles that come up in your life. Acknowledging the problem is the first step because then you can figure out what you need to do to fix it. If your boyfriend breaks up with you, for instance, of course you'll be devastated – but you can't force him to change his mind and want to be with you. What you can do is make a plan to move on, starting by putting one foot in front of the other so you can take the first steps towards your new future.

I recall a time many years ago, when the Lorna Jane brand was still in its infancy, when I had to draw on this philosophy to see me through a very stressful time. Bill and I had travelled to the United States to market Lorna Jane at a fitness trade show. It was a big deal for us at the time and an exciting move into the international retail market. You can imagine my reaction when the shipment of activewear that we had packaged up and sent to Las Vegas wasn't there when we arrived.

Our shipment had been caught up in customs. There we were on the first day of a four-day convention and our stock was nowhere to be seen.

I could have panicked.
I could have raged to the courier company about the hold up.
I could have threatened to sue them for our potential loss of revenue.
I could have packed my bags and gone home.

I could have reacted in a variety of negative ways, but instead, Bill and I set up our stall with the few samples that we had on us and we got busy talking up Lorna Jane. We spent the first day of the conference telling everyone about our products in the hope that they would come back if or when our stock eventually arrived.

I was a woman on a mission and set about creating a plan to get the stock to Las Vegas. Many, many phone calls later our shipment was finally cleared through customs but it was now stuck in Los Angeles. I haggled with a courier company and eventually convinced them to send a truck from Los Angeles to Las Vegas overnight with our goods on board.

I didn't get much sleep that night and paced the length of the hotel room for hours waiting to catch a glimpse of the truck as it pulled into the car park 16 stories below. It finally arrived at 3am and I was able to catch a few hours of sleep before setting up that morning. As soon as the doors to the conference centre opened, we were there to unpack the boxes and set up the stall ready for business.

It was stressful but we got through because during the whole ordeal I was always thinking two steps ahead, preparing for Plan B, C and D if Plan A fell through.

The silver lining was that we had a sensational response on the second day because the lack of stock had actually built up the demand. In the end it all worked out but I've learned from this experience and now I always pack extra samples with me when we travel to trade shows, just in case.

Mum, Julie, me and Louise, the girls at a family dinner

Sisters... not sure about the matching outfits

swimming with Louise as a baby. I made both of our swimsuits

Mum, Julie and me... still dressing like twins

THE STRENGTH OF FAMILY AND FRIENDS

Behind every great woman you will often find an unwavering support system of family and friends and that is certainly the case for me.

From as far back as I can remember my mum has always been there for me 100% and I have no doubt in my mind that this has been a huge contributing factor in me having the confidence to believe in myself enough to follow my dreams, quit my day job and start Lorna Jane. Even as a small child she encouraged me to do what made me happy, but to also be sensible in my decisions, respectful when it came to money and to always be honest and kind to others. When Bill and I first started employing staff she was the one that worked on weekends doing the payroll and making sure that we dotted our i's and crossed our t's. And even though she says she's retired now, she still pops into head office a couple of days a month to make sure that the payroll and superannuation is exactly how it should be.

I am extremely close to my family and it makes sense that they have played an important role in shaping me, my life and Lorna Jane. My sister Julie spent years sewing tights for Lorna Jane on her overlocker when her daughter Louise was a baby. Her partner Ronnie worked alongside Bill building our shops in the early days and now looks after the maintenance of our 100-plus stores. And my niece, Louise, is a talented photographer who works casually in our design room and also took some of the great images for this book.

Looking back, my family has always been there in the background for the good times and the bad. There to celebrate the victories, but more importantly, first with an encouraging word when things haven't gone my way or some friendly advice when a difficult decision needs to be made.

Together with my husband Bill, they have been my unwavering support system, my cheer squad, my back-up plan. And I hope they realise how instrumental they have been in giving me the courage to believe in myself and to never, never, never give up.

my sister Julie and I on a family holiday in the UK

THE POWER OF PEOPLE

No matter how driven and determined you are and no matter how much you believe in yourself, it's impossible to reach your goals if you mingle with miserable, negative people that drag you down.

It's important to surround yourself with positive, like-minded people who support you on this journey we call life. There could be people in your life who undermine and try to sabotage your goals. Let me warn you, these people may not do it in an obvious way but in a manner where they are seemingly supporting you whilst questioning your dreams and making you doubt yourself at the same time.

You can't afford to have these people in your life and in my experience it is better to remove them from your world completely. Friendships – any relationships, in fact – should enrich your life and should be built on mutual love and respect, and a genuine desire to see each other succeed and achieve great things in life.

If someone in your life tries to persuade you to give up on your dreams, even if they are thinking they are acting in your best interest, stand firm on your goals. It can take incredible self-belief and determination to ignore their opinion, especially if it's coming from someone important to you.

In my early 20s I was teaching aerobics at World Gym. The owner was lovely and supportive, letting me have space to create my garments as well as a room to lead my classes. He's also the same guy who offered me work on the reception desk while I was getting the business off the ground, so I felt he was always on my side.

After a year or two of selling my designs out of a fitness centre I realised that my idea of designing fashionable activewear had serious potential, so I decided to open a shopfront in Brisbane city. I was excited about giving my business a proper go and opening my own store – finally, it felt as if my little hobby had turned into a "real" business.

I walked into the gym owner's office and told him I was planning to take a retail lease in the city. He had been a mentor to me over the years and I was excited to share my plans with him. To my surprise, he instantly tried to convince me not to go. He thought the idea was crazy and would lead to more stress than I could handle, and he gave me all sorts of reasons as to why I was better off staying small.

"You've got a great little business, you can come and go as you please," he said. "Why would you want to open a shop where you have to stand around all day, even when you've got no customers? You're taking a huge risk – why not keep going as you are? Your business is great as it is."

Looking back now, I think he was drawing from his own experiences because at the time, his business was facing some challenges. Building a business and taking on staff, and then having to rely on other people, can be tough. He didn't want me to face the same difficulties as him so his protests were coming from a positive place – but I don't think he realised that he was squashing my dreams by voicing his concerns.

I left his office and burst into tears, feeling utterly dejected. It crossed my mind that I should listen to him. He was smarter and more business-savvy than me and had my best interests at heart. I felt he didn't believe in me and at the time, I needed all the encouragement I could get.

I quickly reminded myself that you only get one chance at life and if you don't want to sing the "should have, could have, would have" song when you're old and grey, you have to be willing to back yourself. I decided to move forward with my plans and when I look back, I'm proud of myself for making the decision to go against the advice of someone who, at the time, was very important to me.

Ten years later he called me to tell me he was proud of what I'd achieved and to apologise for trying to discourage me. I hope he realised how much it meant to me that he recognised I had been successful in trying to inspire other women to be the best versions of themselves – and that it had been worth the risk after all.

I find myself in a position now where I can't tell anyone *not* to follow their dreams. The way I see it, if you want to quit your 9 to 5 so you can go and sell bikinis in Bali, then what's stopping you? You can always go back to doing what you were doing beforehand if it doesn't work out.

When my journey began and I was working as a dental therapist, it was Bill who actually reminded me, "You can always go back to dentistry in a few years if Lorna Jane doesn't take off." Having that support from Bill and my family and friends has been crucial in allowing me to achieve the success I enjoy today. That's why I believe it's vital to surround yourself with positive people. Like attracts like, so it makes sense to spend your time with people who inspire you to be the best possible version of yourself.

As well as surrounding yourself with positive people, it's also just as important that they are honest with you. There's nothing worse than people who just agree with you regardless. You want to know that when someone has an opinion, it's authentic – even if you don't always agree with them. That's the culture we've created at Lorna Jane as we encourage everyone to say what they truly think, no matter how silly, outrageous or controversial it may be, knowing that they won't ever be judged for it.

Cairns Lorna Jane team

Sydney Lorna Jane team

Adelaide Lorna Jane team

Filex Fitness Expo

TRUE FRIENDS BRING OUT THE BEST IN YOU

Rae Felesina, Lorna's best friend

Lorna is my closest friend. In fact, she's been my best friend since primary school. She's also technically my boss, as I work as an administration officer at Lorna Jane. I love working for a company that has such a positive environment, empowers women to be the best they can be and promotes a healthy lifestyle.

I have watched my friend grow Lorna Jane from the spark of an idea to the successful business it is today and I couldn't be more proud of everything she's achieved. I've been on this journey with her since the early days and we've shared some memorable moments.

When we lived together, we used to sit on our lounge room floor and cut out patterns for Lorna's orders. I am literally scarred from those days; I wound up with a pair of scissors in my knee and several stitches, all for the love of my friend and the Lorna Jane brand. I also remember working on reception at the original Kelvin Grove office and wearing sunglasses in the afternoon because there wasn't any money to spend on blinds to prevent the sun from streaming in.

As well as being a person with extremely high personal morals, Lorna is encouraging, positive and is determined to make a difference. She is there for me unconditionally and I can't remember a time in my life when she wasn't in it. When people ask me, "How do you deal with her success and all that she has accomplished?" my answer is always the same – "I stand in Lorna's light, not in her shadow".

RAE FELESINA

"I stand in Lorna's light, not in her shadow."

Sunday bike ride

Girls night out

MY BEST FRIEND IS THE ONE WHO BRINGS OUT THE BEST IN ME.

- HENRY FORD

THE CULTURE OF LORNA JANE

Bill and I have worked hard to build a young, vibrant, creative team and we're so proud of the culture we've developed throughout the Lorna Jane business, from the factory floor to the team "behind the scenes" in head office, to the girls working in the stores.

People are attracted to Lorna Jane because of what our brand represents and we've found that when we're recruiting new staff, people come to us in the hope of changing their life, rather than just getting a job. I get to come in to work every day and do what I love to do and we attract employees who believe in the same philosophy.

Bill and I are personally involved in all aspects of the business, so much so that up until recently, I was the fit model for every item of clothing we made. I am still in every single fitting for each new product, tugging at seams and changing lengths, which is no easy task – we create new collections of between 70 and 100 garments every single month.

I still hand-sketch every one of my designs, which drives my production team crazy, but it's the way I like to do it. I sketch and then they input it into Illustrator, and that's how the design process flows. I believe it's these small touches that keep the Lorna Jane brand authentic; and despite our growth, we are still very much a family business.

Bill and I figured out long ago that we couldn't do everything ourselves, as much as we might like to. I realised it was vital that I allowed other people to help me if I wanted the brand to reach its potential.

It was challenging for me at first because I wanted every single customer that went into a Lorna Jane store to feel as if they had been served by me. My aim was for them to get the friendly service and product knowledge that I would give them. Selecting staff and training them up has always been as important to me as choosing the right fabric or designing the perfect pair of pants.

When we recruit we ideally want people to be our brand ambassadors and to grow with the business. We have a number of employees who have been with us since the beginning, and others who have been with us for over a decade. Then we've got people like Danielle in marketing. She was a customer first and then she worked in our stores while she was studying marketing at university. She quickly worked her way up the ranks to become store manager and today, she works in our marketing department at head office.

Lorna Jane dance troupe

Brisbane bridge climb

Bill and I

100th store celebration

DANIELLE McKENZIE

"If your heart is in the right place, with enough hard work, anything is possible."

Danielle McKenzie, Marketing Manager, Lorna Jane

I'm a firm believer that life is not about finding yourself, it is an opportunity to make, and give, something of yourself. Growing up I was innately very shy. Those who know me now find this impossible to believe. As I matured, I came out of my shell and learnt to appreciate my own abilities. Whilst I don't think I was ever naturally talented in any particular field, what I became good at was hard work. In time, with a lot of hard work came a sense of confidence in social, academic and sporting fields.

When I was presented with an opportunity to work for Lorna Jane in my teens I was so excited. As an avid customer I was passionate about both the product and its values. I started my career as a junior sales assistant and within a few months I was managing the Chermside store. I balanced the full-time position whilst studying marketing and journalism at Queensland University of Technology. I enjoyed studying and transferring my knowledge of marketing to the retail environment. Working in our Lorna Jane stores provided me with an invaluable experience. I befriended the many faces of the women of Lorna Jane: the gym bunny whose new LJ tights helped motivate her to train twice a day; the mother-daughter duo who were brought together by their love of Lorna Jane; the courageous woman who had battled breast cancer and gained confidence in wearing our Pammy Crop; the woman on her weightloss journey, a little unsure of LJExcel at first but quickly convinced after first wear; and the older woman surprised this whippersnapper knew what she was talking about! Whilst every woman was different, they were united by a belief that being active empowered their lives.

I stayed at Lorna Jane Chermside for three years whilst completing my degree, at which point I had decided to pursue a career in journalism in Sydney. I set a move date, handed in my resignation, trained up my replacement and packed my bags. One week before I was due to leave, an opportunity to join the marketing team at Lorna Jane HQ became available. Three days later I was meeting Lorna and the team and decided it was too good an opportunity to pass up. When I began working at Lorna Jane HQ, Lorna and Bill headed up a very tight ship. Our team was small but craved success. Like anyone entering the industry, I began at the bottom, which meant I was responsible for my fair share of administrative tasks but I took pride in executing every one to the nth degree. Being part of a small team also meant I was able to contribute to the grand plan. In 2009, my then-marketing manager left Lorna Jane and I took it upon myself to step up and manage the job at hand. At such a young age I was both excited and anxious about the responsibilities this entailed. I distinctly remember a conversation with Bill when he formally asked me to head up the department. I turned to him and said, "I don't have all of the answers but I promise that I will always go looking for them". Over the next 12 months the team doubled in size and I played my part in something special; business was thriving and Lorna Jane was going from strength to strength.

Now as Marketing Manager, I play an integral role in the look and feel of the Lorna Jane brand and communicating our message of *Move, Nourish, Believe*. I am passionate about learning, researching and synthesising information and creating concepts that are as beautiful as they are meaningful and innovative. I love to connect the dots and look at the larger social and cultural trends, and Lorna Jane allows me to combine these passions. I continually challenge myself to push beyond the boundaries and I am nurtured through an environment that encourages me to think outside the box. Lorna Jane is not just a brand. It is a belief system to which I subscribed long ago. I come to work knowing that I am helping women to enrich their lives, and that is why I LOVE my job. I'd be lying if I said I didn't have those moments when I still doubt my own ability but just as I had learned earlier in life, if your heart is in the right place, with enough hard work, anything is possible.

WHAT DO YOU BELIEVE IN?

I've always had a clear vision of what I wanted out of my life and I've been fortunate enough to tick off every single goal I ever set out to achieve. So what do you believe in and what is it you want to achieve in your life? More importantly, what is holding you back and preventing you from reaching your goals? Once you work out what is standing in your way, you can create a game plan to push through the challenges in front of you and work towards living the life you've always dreamed of. It's tempting to compare yourself to others but that never gets you very far, so my advice is to go on your own journey without competing against anyone else and set yourself a clear vision filled with hope, passion and purpose. Remember to aim high, be positive and dream as big as your imagination allows – I'm living proof that if you can dream it, you can most definitely achieve it.

EVERY NOW AND THEN, **BITE OFF** MORE TH

POSITIVE THINGS HAPPEN TO **POSITIVE PEOPLE**.

DON'T FOLLOW YOUR DREAMS, CHA

KNOWING WHAT YOU WANT IS THE **FIRST STEP** T

BELIEVE IN THE BEAUTY OF YOUR **DREAMS**. - ELEANOR R

DESIGN A **LIFE** THAT YOU **LOVE**.

LIVE LIKE CRAZY.

LISTEN TO YOUR **HEART** ABOVE ALL **OTHER V**

LOVE LIFE AND IT WILL LOVE YOU RIGH

NOTHING IS IMPOSSIBLE TO A WILLING HEART. - JOHN KEYWOOD

ENTHUSIASM **MOVES** THE WORLD. - ARTHUR JAMES BALFOUR

IT IS **NEVER TOO LATE** TO BECOME WHA

LIFE IS A DARING ADVENTURE OR NOTHING. - HELE

EVERY **BIG CHANGE** STARTS WITH A **SINGLE STEP**.

THERE IS NO SUCH THING IN ANYONE'S LIFE AS AN UNIMPORTAN

THOSE WHO **WISH TO SING** ALWAYS **FIND A SONG**. -

IT'S NICE TO BE IMPORTANT, BUT IT'S IMPOR

OU CAN CHEW. - SIR THOMAS BROWN

RAH BEENY

HEM. - ANON

RD GETTING IT. - MAE WEST

VELT

S. - MARTA KAGAN

ACK.

U MIGHT HAVE BEEN. - GEORGE ELLIOT

LLER

- ALEXANDER WOOLLCOTT

DISH PROVERB

T TO BE NICE. - JOHN CASSIS

Q & A WITH LORNA JANE

- -

One of the things I love most about the Lorna Jane brand is the connectivity we have with our customers. Social media has provided us with a fantastic opportunity to interact with these people but even long before Facebook existed we were always reaching out to our customers and asking for their input and feedback.

If I see someone on the street wearing Lorna Jane, I'll stop and ask them what they like about the products, what they would change and what they'd like to see us do next. There's no better way to grow and learn than by connecting with the people who actually wear our clothes, so whether someone takes the time to comment on our Facebook page, make a suggestion in store, or send feedback through our website or on email, it all gets taken into account during the design and production process.

On that note, I'd like to share some questions I received via Facebook from some of our loyal customers. Nothing inspires me more than hearing your incredible stories of being healthy and living an active life, so feel free to share at www.facebook.com/lornajane.active.

Love,

Lorna Jane xx

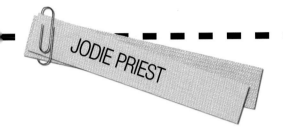

JODIE PRIEST

What is your inspiration to get out of bed every day?

Pure and simple; I love the life I have created and chosen for myself. I get to wake up every day and go to work and do what I love to do. To be honest, getting up for me is the easy part – it's the going-to-bed part, where I have things I want to do and millions of ideas in my head, that I struggle with! My advice: if you're unhappy with your career path, be bold and brave enough to change your direction and therefore your destiny. I did it 21 years ago and entered into an industry I knew nothing about. While some pegged it as a risky move, I made the choice on my own and have never looked back.

What's one piece of advice you would give to any woman anywhere in the world?

You have the ability to create the life that you want to lead, so stop listening to the people in the grandstands who try and tell you who you are and what you want to be. One of the most empowering ideas in this world is that you have the right to change your mind and change your life. Nothing is impossible. It doesn't matter where you come from or what you do, if you have a dream, it is possible to make it a reality and live the life you imagined.

AMANDA ROSE

How do you relax and stay grounded without getting caught up in the glamour part of your world?

I love the world of fashion. I've always found the glitz and glamour fascinating. However, I'm happy to keep it at arms length. There are certain events I wouldn't miss but I work full-time at Lorna Jane and I need to be focused on the brand and the product we are designing each day. If I went to every party and function I wouldn't be able to concentrate on my business so I'm selective about what I support and attend. I also think part of staying grounded is having time to relax. You need to take time out to care for yourself and your spirit. If you look at relaxing as an opportunity to rejuvenate and revitalise, you will never get caught up in the negatives of a high-profile life because when you think of actions that nourish your soul, they are often not materialistic – and that is what I concentrate on. If I'm going for a massage, I don't think of it as "pampering," I see it as something that my body deserves as a thank you for carrying me around all day and enduring my work-outs. When you are true to yourself and live a genuine life filled with all the unique things that you as an individual love to do, you won't be overwhelmed by the "glamour" side of things as you will be comfortable in your own skin and who you are.

BELINDA NORTON-SMITH

MEGAN McCUTCHEON

How do you remain focused when life's problems take up time and energy?

The mind is a very powerful thing. For me, I just decide that something isn't a problem, it's a challenge. I am a positive person and this attitude has helped me get through times in my life that others often say must have been very difficult. I just refuse to buy into it. When you concentrate on problems and the negatives of a situation, you become stressed and agitated and you're only harming yourself. Rather than take the "woe is me" approach, I refuse to be a victim and instead I find it's much better to make a plan of how to deal with something. I simply think, "Well, this has happened, there is nothing I can do about it but I can certainly try to make sure it doesn't happen again and I can make a plan for how to make everything better." My attitude is: I can overcome anything as long as I have a plan.

What could you not live without?

I think I am strong enough to "live" without anything. However, there are certain things I have in my life that if lost would impact the way I feel. Apart from family of course, being active is something I would certainly go to all lengths to maintain. It has become such a big part of who I am spiritually that I would not like to think of my life without being able to move. This idea is grounding and makes me grateful for each and every day that I wake up feeling healthy and energised.

CATHERINE FORSYTH

ANN MATTHEWS

Who inspires you the most and why?

There are so many people who inspire me. I think what's important about having a number of influencers in your life is that you are still free to be your own person but can benefit from the experience, advice and knowledge of others. I am inspired by amazing fashion designers like Phoebe Philo and Valentino, however I am just as inspired by athletes who push beyond their limits, like Stephanie Gilmore and Lance Armstrong. The other people who inspire me each and every day are the women who have been inspired to change their lives for the better and get fit and healthy. We have so many customers who say that Lorna Jane has inspired them to lose weight, change their career or made them more determined to fight an illness such as cancer. Little do they know that while we may inspire them through our positive brand image and messages, they also inspire us.

If you could only take five items in your overnight bag, what would they be?

This requires careful consideration! If space were not an issue, I'd take five friends and family; otherwise I'd take the following: toothbrush and toothpaste (you can't have worked in dental hygiene and not be forever paranoid about tooth decay); my iPad (to keep me "in touch" and entertained); a pair of running shoes for a morning walk or jog; some Lorna Jane full-length tights suitable for exercise or relaxation; and my dog Roger (he comes with me whenever possible).

RUTH McCONNELL TREVASKIS

How do you maintain motivation on days when you feel like you have none?

Motivation is one thing that people seem to align with physical activity but I believe you need to feel motivated and energised in every single part of your life. As such, I feel motivated by knowing I am doing everything I can in order to live a full and happy life. When you are looking forward to something you don't require motivation to do it. I treat my work-outs in the same way. I make them enjoyable so I look forward to doing them and stay motivated. I love to walk my dog, I want to hit the gym in my new activewear outfit, and I want to attend my yoga class because I get to catch up with my friend afterwards. It's not hard to find the fun in fitness – you just need to look a little harder sometimes. Another tip is to plan out your week so you can look forward to everything. Having a plan is what gives me a sense of control and peace in this crazy world we live in. I flourish when I have a routine. By mapping out what I am going to do I don't need to muster motivation, I'm simply excited about doing it and enjoying it along the way.

KRISTY HARDEY

What music do you listen to when you work-out?

I love John Mayer. His star may have fallen over the last couple of years and some may even view his music as too mainstream, but this is the perfect example of me living my own life, without caring about what other people think. I love his laid-back, cool music and that's what counts. His smooth voice and great guitar skills are perfect for a relaxing walk or morning stretching session.

Brains, beauty and success? How do you do that?

I am a firm believer that women can have and do it all. It is an attitude that has served me well over the past 20 years and hopefully the next 20 years to come. But what is important to note is that nothing comes without work. If you want to create a different life, be willing to work at it. If you want brains, be willing to educate yourself and be dedicated to becoming a lifelong learner. For me this is about reading as many books as I can. For beauty, do things to nourish your body and understand your strengths and it will fall into place. If you eat well and exercise, you can improve the health of your skin, hair, nails and teeth as well as having a great body. Don't worry about what others say. People are always telling me to cut my hair short but I love my long hair. It's part of who I am and I love the way it makes me feel. For success, you need to be passionate about what you do. I feel people talk about this all the time but the sentiment of "do what you love and success will follow" couldn't be closer to the truth. Shut out the naysayers and make the choice to do what you love. If you feel you cannot do what you love full-time, then bring it into your life as a permanent hobby. You will find you are more engaged in your work simply because you know that doing well in your job is what allows you to do what you love in your spare time.

JOANNE MANCUSO

when you were a little girl, what did you want to "be" when you grew up?

Like all women, I wanted to be so many things: a ballet dancer, an actress, a journalist. However, I think it's important to point out that I didn't really ever decide to be a fashion designer, I just fell into it. Once I discovered it, I realised I had a true passion for fitness and fashion and I could offer the world something that others could not. It's good to remember that sometimes you need to live a little in order to discover what your great passion is. Don't put pressure on yourself to find something. Chances are it is already staring you in the face or it will happen when you least expect it.

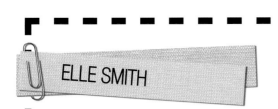

KRISTI JAREMUS

ELLE SMITH

which business leaders inspire you to achieve more, especially women business leaders?

I try not to look at other businesses too much as I want to be sure we are operating in a way that is unique and authentic. However, there are a couple of influential people who inspire me, such as Steve Jobs and Richard Branson. Both these entrepreneurs have had the courage to be themselves and despite achieving success they push the realms of the business world and continually strive to be better. I'm also inspired by women like Cate Blanchett, who is high profile but continues to live a more centred and normal existence. For an award-winning actress with three young boys, no nanny and a successful career, and who is an advocate for Australian film and actions against climate change, she is someone I hold in high regard.

When you are sick or feeling blue or you're having a bad day, how do you stay focused and healthy?

I can honestly say that I don't often have "low" or "bad" days. This wasn't always the case but I believe it is a direct result of eating a clean, healthy and nutritious diet and maintaining an active lifestyle. The way in which healthy living can impact on your psyche is completely underrated. By eating a balanced diet free from refined and over-processed foods, you will have balanced moods. By getting into the fresh air and going for a walk, you will have space, mental clarity and focus. I always say that when I run I lose my breath, but find my answers.

DIMITY EMERY

If you had the chance to go back would you do anything differently?

I would not change a thing. While my life has had its challenges, I believe these challenges create the person you are. Without them, you lose perspective and the wins never taste as sweet. I try not to look back or live in the past. You can't change what has happened but you certainly can benefit from looking forward and deciding where you want to be and take steps to get there.

LAURA GANGEMI

MEL REGAN

FIONA TYE

Have you ever got to a point in your life where you didn't know what your next goal was or you felt directionless?

I think everybody experiences this from time to time but it is about moving onwards and upwards and setting goals that you can work towards. If you're feeling trapped at work and you're not too sure where to move, don't feel the pressure to set a goal in your work life and instead set one in your personal life. Why not decide you are going to learn to run 5km without stopping? In just moving forward with focus and starting to achieve, you will find you might actually gain clarity on other things that are going on in your life.

If you were able to have coffee with anyone in the world, who would it be and why?

There are so many people I'd like to have a coffee with. I think the two most famous would be Michelle Obama, to discuss her time spent influencing the children of America and her exercise regime, and Oprah, just to talk about her journey and how she got to where she is today. But if neither of them were available for coffee then I would be more than happy chatting to my customers. I could discuss life and its challenges, triumphs and tribulations with the women who buy my clothes for hours. These women are out there living real life and striving to achieve great things. They are testament to what Lorna Jane stands for and they are endorsing the *Move Nourish Believe* philosophy.

THOSE WHO DARE AND DARE GREATLY ARE THOSE WHO ACHIEVE.

MOVE.
NOURISH.
BELIEVE.

WHERE TO FROM HERE

ALL OUR DREAMS COME TRUE IF WE HAVE THE COURAGE TO PURSUE THEM.

- WALT DISNEY

In the first half of 2011, we celebrated a very significant milestone in the Lorna Jane journey: the opening of our 100th store in Little Collins Street, Melbourne.

It was a huge achievement for us and I have to admit, it crept up on me. Sometimes I'm so busy working on the "nuts and bolts" of the business, sketching designs, creating new concepts and brainstorming with my marketing team, that I have to physically force myself to stop, take a breather and acknowledge what's happening and what Lorna Jane has become.

I am surrounded by a wonderful team of people who are living and breathing the Lorna Jane dream with me and who support our vision 110%. They not only keep me motivated but they're also only too happy to remind me when we have achieved something special and it's time to celebrate.

When we realised the launch of our 100th store was fast approaching, we decided to mark the occasion with a nationwide roadshow tour. I visited Lorna Jane stores in Brisbane, Sydney, Melbourne, Cairns, Adelaide and Perth. After months spent in the design room, it was fun to get out there and connect with the Lorna Jane staff and meet loyal customers. Before hitting the road I knew people were passionate about Lorna Jane, but meeting them face to face and seeing how they live and breathe the *Move, Nourish, Believe* philosophy in their own lives was incredibly humbling and inspiring.

On one particular night I made my way to our roadshow event in Brisbane with our brand manager. We hopped into the lift and as we made our way up through the layers of the building, the lift stopped and three girls jumped in – I couldn't help but notice they were all dressed head-to-toe in Lorna Jane.

The thrill of seeing people wearing my designs never fades. There are so many brands to choose from and the fact that someone will go out and purposefully choose to purchase something I've conceptualised, designed and created makes me so grateful. It's a satisfying feeling because I feel we've connected in some way; I feel they understand what I was thinking about when I first began sketching it.

These girls had just finished working out and I was desparate to interact with them. It took every bit of restraint to stop me from asking them outright, "What made you pick that crop top, and what's you're favourite thing about those leggings?" Instead, I made a couple of vague comments about the gym to try and get the dialogue going but the girls didn't respond so I left it at that.

Off we went to the roadshow and as the event kicked off, I told the team instore about our encounter in the lift. I was thrilled to share with everyone that we'd seen three women proudly wearing Lorna Jane. One of our team members asked if the girls had recognised me and I said, "No, and I'm disappointed because I wanted to chat with them."

The next day I arrived back to work at our head office in Fortitude Valley and Sam, our social media guru, called me over. "Hey, at the roadshow last night, did you happen to use the lift at Wintergarden shopping centre?" he asked.

He nodded towards his computer screen and showed me that someone had written on our Facebook page 'OMG – I think I was in a lift with Lorna Jane last night! I can't believe it!'

It's moments like these when I have to pinch myself because that's when I realise how far I've come. From cutting out patterns by hand and stitching them together myself in an old sewing room, creating leotards for friends, to opening our 100th store. It's been a wild ride, and it's not over yet.

So what's the next step on the Lorna Jane journey? I'm always seeing new opportunities – sometimes I wish I could turn my brain off but one of my friends once said to me, "Lorna, you can never turn it off, it's who you are." I've come to accept that my mind is always going to race ahead at a hundred miles an hour. I'm not the best sleeper in the world because I can't switch off easily, which is why I keep a book next to my bed. Sometimes my best and brightest ideas strike at 3am in the morning.

At the moment, we have more than 100 Lorna Jane stores across Australia and we've begun expanding internationally. We recently opened a Lorna Jane concept store in South Africa and our sights are now firmly set on the United States.

In a way, it feels like we've come full circle because by launching into new territories, we will be going back to our roots and starting from scratch. Without the benefit of 21 years worth of brand building, we have no reputation in these new markets. We are taking a risk but what's the worst that can happen? We open some new stores and they don't work. The way I see it, if we want to achieve big things, we have to aim as high as we possibly can.

SWAPPING PERFECTION FOR HAPPINESS

No one is perfect, yet in the past I have found myself striving for just that, even though I knew it was not achievable. These days, my mantra is never to aim for perfection but to simply aim to be the best version of myself. When I'm tempted to venture down that perfection path, I remind myself that instead of striving to be (and making everything around me) perfect, I need to keep in mind that being happy and content is the most important goal.

I'm blessed to have a beautiful life and I'm grateful to wake up and spend my days doing what I do. It is my passion to design activewear that makes women look as good as they feel and the highest compliment I can receive is when a woman chooses to wear Lorna Jane.

I want my designs to inspire women to be active and as an extension of that, I want women to live their best life through the *Move, Nourish, Believe* philosophy. I've dedicated my life to spreading the message of active living far and wide and while I'm proud of how much we've achieved with Lorna Jane we still have so far to go.

There's a whole new generation of young women to share my message with and I want Lorna Jane to be there for them, to inspire and motivate them to be energetic, optimistic, confident and hopeful that they can achieve any goal they set their mind to. A friend of mine once told me that her daughter confessed, "Mum, I think if I start wearing Lorna Jane I will actually feel like exercising." If only she knew how happy that made me.

Sometimes, I can't believe that all of this started when I ripped apart one swimsuit on my dining room table more than two decades ago. But it did happen and I am living, breathing proof that any good idea can flourish if you believe it is possible.

My philosophy of *Move, Nourish, Believe* can be such a powerful tool in your life. It's simple, easy to follow, and most importantly, it works.

You need to move everyday. No excuses. Eat food that nourishes your body. Be positive and believe in your ability to live an extraordinary life.

Choose to Never, Never, Never Give Up and don't give yourself a hard time over that indulgent chocolate bar or skipped gym session because you are only human and the next positive decision you make is just around the corner. Tomorrow is another day and the first day of your new and invigorating life. You just have to reach out and grab it.

Love,

Lorna Jane xx

STYLISH!
I lorna jane
because...
it Supports my active life
because...
towards a NEW+ life!
because...
I AM READY TO Perform!!
because...
EMPOWERS WOMEN
GET ACTIVE!!
because...
FEEL

encouraged me
take a step towards
BETTER ME ♥

because...
The Pammy

I ♡

because...
it makes...
☺

I ♡ lorna jane

because...
I FEEL MOTIVATED FOR
MY MORNING RUN

I ♡ lorna jane

because...

I ♡ lorna ja

because...
WITH LJ, I MOVE